THE ULTIMATE
COLORADO ROCKIES
TRIVIA BOOK

A Collection of Amazing Trivia Quizzes
and Fun Facts for Die-Hard Rockies Fans!

Ray Walker

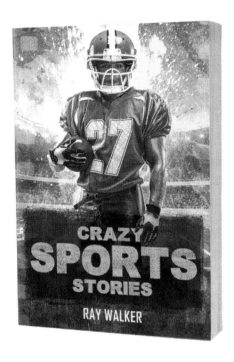

CONTENTS

INTRODUCTION

The Colorado Rockies were established in 1993 as an MLB expansion team. Even though they are a relatively new team in professional baseball, they have consistently proven themselves to be a team that fights hard and is a force to be reckoned with.

Although the Colorado Rockies have not yet won the coveted World Series championship or National League West Division title, they have won a National League pennant and earned five wild card berths. They made their only World Series appearance in 2007 against the Boston Red Sox. Their most recent postseason appearance came in 2018 when they won a wild card berth.

The Colorado Rockies have retired the uniform numbers of Todd Helton and of course, Jackie Robinson. Larry Walker's number will be retired in the summer of 2021.

The Colorado Rockies' current home is Coors Field, which opened in 1995. They play in one of the most difficult divisions in baseball, the National League West, alongside the Los Angeles Dodgers, San Diego Padres, Arizona Diamondbacks, and San Francisco Giants.

The thing about baseball is that it is a lot like life. There are good times and bad times, good days and bad days, but you have to do your absolute best to never give up. The Colorado Rockies have proven that they refuse to give up and that they will do anything they need to do to bring a championship to the state of Colorado. Winning is more than possible when you have a storied past like the Colorado Rockies. They have so much captivating history and so many undeniable player legacies to be profoundly proud of.

With such a storied team past that spans decades, you're probably already very knowledgeable as the die-hard Rockies fan that you are. Let's test that knowledge to see if you truly are the World's Biggest Rockies fan.

All stats in this book are current as of the end of the 2020 season.

CHAPTER 1:

ORIGINS & HISTORY

QUIZ TIME!

1. What other team name did the Colorado Rockies franchise once go by?

   a. Colorado Corn Huskers
   b. Colorado Expos
   c. Colorado Brewers
   d. They have always been the Colorado Rockies

2. In what year was the Colorado Rockies franchise established?

   a. 1973
   b. 1983
   c. 1993
   d. 2003

3. The Colorado Rockies' current home stadium is Coors Field.

   a. True
   b. False

4. Which division do the Colorado Rockies play in?

   a. American League West
   b. National League West
   c. American League Central
   d. National League Central

5. The Colorado Rockies have never won a wild card berth.

   a. True
   b. False

6. How many National League Pennants have the Colorado Rockies won?

   a. 0
   b. 1
   c. 2
   d. 3

7. Who is (or are) the current principal owner(s) of the Colorado Rockies?

   a. Larry Dolan
   b. Robert Nutting
   c. Richard and Charles Monfort
   d. Arturo Moreno

8. Who is the winningest manager in Colorado Rockies history?

   a. Don Baylor
   b. Walt Weiss
   c. Bud Black
   d. Clint Hurdle

9. What is the name of the Colorado Rockies' Triple-A Team and where is it located?

    a. Albuquerque Isotopes
    b. Jacksonville Jumbo Shrimp
    c. Toledo Mud Hens
    d. Nashville Sounds

10. Who was the first manager of the Colorado Rockies?

    a. Jim Leyland
    b. Don Baylor
    c. Buddy Bell
    d. Jim Tracy

11. The Colorado Rockies were members of the American League West from 1993 through 2005.

    a. True
    b. False

12. What is the name of the Colorado Rockies' spring training home stadium?

    a. Goodyear Ballpark
    b. Hohokam Stadium
    c. Salt River Fields
    d. Sloan Park

13. How many appearances have the Rockies made in the MLB playoffs?

    a. 2
    b. 3

c. 4

d. 5

14. How many World Series titles have the Colorado Rockies won?

    a. 0

    b. 1

    c. 2

    d. 3

15. The Colorado Rockies' current manager is Bud Black.

    a. True

    b. False

16. Which stadium was the first home of the Colorado Rockies?

    a. Falcon Stadium

    b. Folsom Field

    c. Mile High Stadium

    d. Coors Field

17. Who is the franchise's current president of baseball operations?

    a. Mike Rizzo

    b. Greg Feasel

    c. David Forst

    d. Thad Levine

18. How many National League West Division titles have the Colorado Rockies won?

    a. 0

    b. 1

c. 2

d. 3

19. The Rockies share Salt River Fields with the Arizona Diamondbacks during spring training.

    a. True

    b. False

20. Richard Monfort is the current president and CEO of the Colorado Rockies.

    a. True

    b. False

QUIZ ANSWERS

1. D – They have always been the Colorado Rockies

2. C – 1993

3. A – True

4. B – National League West

5. B – False (1995, 2007, 2009, 2017, 2018)

6. B – 1 (2007)

7. C – Richard and Charles Monfort

8. D – Clint Hurdle

9. A – Albuquerque Isotopes

10. B – Don Baylor

11. B – False, they have always been in the NL West

12. C – Salt River Fields

13. D – 5

14. A – 0

15. A – True

16. C – Mile High Stadium

17. B – Greg Feasel

18. A – 0

19. A – True

20. A – True

DID YOU KNOW?

1. The Colorado Rockies have had seven managers so far: Don Baylor, Jim Leyland, Buddy Bell, Clint Hurdle, Jim Tracy, Walt Weiss, and Bud Black.

2. The team's current manager is Bud Black. He has been their manager since 2017. He was the Los Angeles Angels pitching coach from 2000-2006 And he was manager of the San Diego Padres from 2007-2015. During his MLB career as a pitcher, he played for the Seattle Mariners, Kansas City Royals, Cleveland Indians, Toronto Blue Jays, and San Francisco Giants. He attended San Diego State University and graduated with a bachelor's degree in management in 1979. He was named the 2010 National League Manager of the Year Award. He won one World Series as a player with the Kansas City Royals in 1985 and one with the Los Angeles Angels as a coach in 2002.

3. Clint Hurdle is the Colorado Rockies' all-time winningest manager with a record of 534-625 for a .461 winning percentage. Hurdle managed the Colorado Rockies from 2002 to 2009. He has also managed the Pittsburgh Pirates. He was named the National League Manager of the Year in 2013.

4. Richard and Charles Monfort are the current principal owners of the Colorado Rockies. They are brothers whose father once owned Monfort of Colorado Inc. The company

was a meat distribution company that was sold to ConAgra Foods in 1987.

5. The Colorado Rockies hosted the 1998 All-Star Game at Coors Field, the only time the franchise has hosted the event.

6. The Colorado Rockies have had one no-hitter thrown. It was thrown by Ubaldo Jiménez on April 17, 2010, against the Atlanta Braves.

7. Larry Walker's No. 33 retired by the Colorado Rockies on September 25, 2021. He was supposed to have his number retired in 2020 but it was postponed due to the COVID-19 pandemic.

8. The Colorado Rockies' Double-A team is the Hartford Yard Goats. High Single-A is the Spokane Indians. Low Single-A is the Fresno Grizzlies.

9. The Colorado Rockies' mascot is named "Dinger." He is a purple triceratops dinosaur. A dinosaur was chosen for their mascot because dinosaur fossils, including a triceratops skull, were found at the Coors Field site while it was being built.

10. The Colorado Rockies have retired just one number so far; two if you include Jackie Robinson's No. 42, which is retired league-wide. The Rockies retired Todd Helton's No. 17 in 2014.

CHAPTER 2:

JERSEYS AND NUMBERS

QUIZ TIME!

1. The Rockies were the first team in MLB history to wear purple pinstripes.

    a. True

    b. False

2. What are the official team colors?

    a. Purple, silver, white

    b. Purple, black, navy blue

    c. Purple, black, white

    d. Purple, black, silver

3. During the Colorado Rockies' inaugural season, players did not have their names on the backs of their home uniforms.

    a. True

    b. False

4. Which of the following numbers is retired by the Colorado Rockies?

a. 7

b. 17

c. 37

d. 47

5. What number does Charlie Blackmon wear as a member of the Colorado Rockies?

    a. 8

    b. 18

    c. 19

    d. 28

6. What number did Larry Walker wear during his time with the Colorado Rockies?

    a. 3

    b. 11

    c. 22

    d. 33

7. Troy Tulowitzki wore the Nos. 14 and 2 during his time with the Rockies.

    a. True

    b. False

8. Only one Rockies player has ever worn the uniform No. 0. Who is that player?

    a. John Axford

    b. Adam Ottavino

    c. Josh Outman

    d. Phillip Diehl

9. Who is the only Colorado player ever to have worn No. 83?

    a. Matt Herges
    b. Joe Beimel
    c. Josh Outman
    d. Alan Trejo

10. No Colorado Rockies player has ever worn No. 99.

    a. True
    b. False

11. What number did Todd Helton wear with the Rockies?

    a. 7
    b. 17
    c. 27
    d. 37

12. What number did Nolan Arenado wear with the Rockies?

    a. 8
    b. 18
    c. 28
    d. 38

13. Carlos Gonzalez wore No. 5 during with the Colorado Rockies.

    a. True
    b. False

14. What number did Matt Holliday wear as a member of the Colorado Rockies?

a. 5

b. 7

c. 9

d. Both A and B

15. What number does Trevor Story currently wear with the Rockies?

    a. 27

    b. 37

    c. 47

    d. None of the Above

16. What number did Ubaldo Jiménez wear with the Rockies?

    a. 18

    b. 28

    c. 38

    d. 48

17. During his time with the Colorado Rockies, DJ LeMahieu wore which number?

    a. 2

    b. 9

    c. 26

    d. 33

18. What number did Vinny Castilla wear with the Rockies?

    a. 9

    b. 14

    c. 19

    d. Both A and B

19. What number did Justin Morneau wear with the Colorado Rockies?

    a. 11

    b. 22

    c. 33

    d. Both B and C

20. Aaron Cook wore Nos. 35 and 28 during his time with the Colorado Rockies.

    a. True

    b. False

QUIZ ANSWERS

1. A - True
2. D – Purple, black, silver
3. A – True
4. B – 17
5. C – 19
6. D – 33
7. A – True
8. B – Adam Ottavino
9. D – Alan Trejo
10. B – False (Alfredo Amézaga, Darren Clarke, and Turk Wendell all wore it.)
11. B – 17
12. C – 28
13. A – True
14. D – Both A and B
15. A – 27
16. C – 38
17. B – 9
18. A – 9
19. C – 33
20. A – True

DID YOU KNOW?

1. The Colorado Rockies have retired two uniform numbers so far: Todd Helton (No.17) and Jackie Robinson (No. 42). Larry Walker's No. 33 will be retired by the team in September 2021.

2. During his time with the Colorado Rockies, John Vander Wal wore No. 35.

3. Jason Giambi wore No. 23 during his time with the Colorado Rockies.

4. During his time with the Colorado Rockies, Eric Young Sr. wore No. 21.

5. During his time with the Colorado Rockies, Joe Girardi wore No. 7.

6. During his time with the Colorado Rockies, Walt Weiss wore No. 22.

7. Jackie Robinson's No. 42 is retired by the Colorado Rockies as well as the MLB as a whole. No Rockies or MLB player will ever wear No. 42 again. The Yankees' Mariano Rivera was the final player to wear it.

8. During his time with the Colorado Rockies, Seth Smith wore Nos. 12, 25, and 7.

9. During his time with the Colorado Rockies, Huston Street wore No. 16.

10. During his time with the Colorado Rockies, Jason Hammel wore No. 46.

CHAPTER 3:

THE TODDFATHER

QUIZ TIME!

1. How old was Todd Helton when he made his MLB debut?

   a. 20

   b. 21

   c. 22

   d. 23

2. Todd Helton played his entire 17-season MLB career with the Colorado Rockies.

   a. True

   b. False

3. Where was Todd Helton born?

   a. Nashville, TN

   b. Knoxville, TN

   c. Thornton, CO

   d. Broomfield, CO

4. When was Todd Helton born?

a. April 20, 1973

b. April 20, 1983

c. August 20, 1973

d. August 20, 1983

5. Todd Helton did NOT win a World Series championship during his MLB career.

a. True

b. False

6. How many All-Star Games was Todd Helton named to?

a. 2

b. 3

c. 5

d. 8

7. What year was Todd Helton drafted by the Colorado Rockies?

a. 1995

b. 1997

c. 1999

d. 2000

8. Todd Helton's full name is Todd Lynn Helton.

a. True

b. False

9. What is Todd Helton's career batting average?

a. .286

b. .296

c. .306

d. .316

10. How many times was Todd Helton named NL MVP?

    a. 0

    b. 1

    c. 2

    d. 3

11. How many Gold Glove Awards did Todd Helton win?

    a. 1

    b. 2

    c. 3

    d. 4

12. Todd Helton won the 2000 MLB batting title.

    a. True

    b. False

13. How many Silver Slugger Awards did Todd Helton win?

    a. 1

    b. 2

    c. 3

    d. 4

14. Todd Helton won the NL Hank Aaron Award in 2000.

    a. True

    b. False

15. How many home runs did Todd Helton hit?

a. 349

b. 359

c. 369

d. 379

16. How many bases did Todd Helton steal?

    a. 37

    b. 77

    c. 107

    d. 207

17. Todd Helton's career WAR is 61.8.

    a. True

    b. False

18. How many times was Todd Helton named the NL Player of the Month?

    a. 1

    b. 2

    c. 3

    d. 4

19. How many hits did Todd Helton record?

    a. 1,519

    b. 2,119

    c. 2,519

    d. 3,119

20. Todd Helton was the MLB RBI Leader in 2000.

    a. True

    b. False

QUIZ ANSWERS

1. D – 23

2. A – True

3. B – Knoxville, TN

4. C – August 20, 1973

5. A – True

6. C – 5

7. A – 1995

8. A – True

9. D - .316

10. A – 0

11. C – 3

12. A – True

13. D – 4

14. A – True

15. C – 369

16. A – 37

17. A - True

18. D – 4 (May 2000, August 2000, May 2002, April 2003)

19. C – 2,519

20. A – True

DID YOU KNOW?

1. Todd Helton was a teammate of Peyton Manning on the University of Tennessee football team. Peyton Manning was the quarterback of the Denver Broncos from 2012 through 2015.

2. Todd Helton wore No. 17 in honor of Chicago Cubs and Arizona Diamondbacks first baseman Mark Grace.

3. So far, Todd Helton has appeared on three National Baseball Hall of Fame ballots. While he has not yet received enough votes to be inducted, he has received enough votes to stay on the ballot.

4. Todd Helton was named the NL Player of the Week six times in his MLB career.

5. Todd Helton had 7,962 at-bats.

6. Todd Helton collected 1,406 RBIs.

7. Todd Helton scored 1,401 runs.

8. Todd Helton holds the Colorado Rockies records for home runs, hits, walks, doubles, RBIs, runs scored, total bases, and games played.

9. Before Todd Helton was drafted by the Colorado Rockies in 1995, he was drafted by the San Diego Padres in 1992. He did not sign and chose to attend college instead.

10. In 2008, Todd Helton was diagnosed with a degenerative back condition that put his playing career in jeopardy. He played his final MLB game on September 29, 2013, against the Los Angeles Dodgers.

CHAPTER 4:

CATCHY NICKNAMES

QUIZ TIME!

1. What nickname does Nolan Arenado go by?

    a. Nado

    b. Sandblaster

    c. Nodo

    d. Both A and B

2. Todd Helton goes by the nickname "\ the Toddfather."

    a. True

    b. False

3. What nickname does Larry Walker go by?

    a. Cougar

    b. Booger

    c. Looker

    d. Smuggler

4. What is Matt Holliday's nickname?

    a. Big Money

    b. Holler

c. Big Daddy

d. Matty Day

5. What nickname does Troy Tulowitzki go by?

a. Triple T

b. Tulo

c. Witty

d. Double T

6. Which nickname does Carlos Gonzalez go by?

a. Crusher

b. Carz

c. Losgo

d. Cargo

7. Ubaldo Jiménez goes by the nicknames "Big U" and "U."

a. True

b. False

8. What nickname does Charlie Blackmon go by?

a. Big Black

b. Charmon

c. Chuck Nazty

d. Nasty Chuck

9. What nickname does DJ LeMahieu go by?

a. Monster

b. Machine

c. Megatron

d. Murder

10. What nickname does Andres Galarraga go by?

    a. Big Bear
    b. Big Mountain
    c. Big Dog
    d. Big Cat

11. What nickname does Bret Saberhagen go by?

    a. Gens
    b. Hags
    c. Sabes
    d. B-Sabe

12. During the 2019 MLB Player's Weekend, Trevor Story went by the nickname "True."

    a. True
    b. False

13. Which nickname does Dexter Fowler go by?

    a. Dexter's Laboratory
    b. Daddy Long Legs
    c. Dex Mex
    d. Fowl Ball

14. What nickname does Jason Hammel go by?

    a. Hot Stuff
    b. Ja-Mel
    c. Ham Man
    d. Hammer

15. Ryan Spilborghs goes by the nickname "Spilly."

a. True

b. False

16. What nickname does Scott Podsednik go by?

    a. Nik

    b. Pod Man

    c. The Podfather

    d. The Platypus

17. Don Baylor went by the nicknames "Groove" and "the Sneak Thief."

    a. True

    b. False

18. "DJ" is a nickname. What is DJ LeMahieu's full name?

    a. Daniel James LeMahieu

    b. David John LeMahieu

    c. Derek Jacob LeMahieu

    d. Dustin Jason LeMahieu

19. What nickname does Craig Counsell go by?

    a. Sheep

    b. Pig

    c. Cow

    d. Chicken

20. Jason Grilli goes by the nickname "Grilled Cheese."

    a. True

    b. False

QUIZ ANSWERS

1. D – Both A and B

2. A – True

3. B – Booger

4. C – Big Daddy

5. B – Tulo

6. D – Cargo

7. A – True

8. C – Chuck Nazty

9. B – Machine

10. D – Big Cat

11. C – Sabes

12. A – True

13. B – Daddy Long Legs

14. D – Hammer

15. B – False

16. C – The Podfather

17. A – True

18. B – David John LeMahieu

19. D – Chicken

20. A – True

DID YOU KNOW?

1. Mark Reynolds goes by the nicknames, "Mega-Mark," "Sheriff of Swattingham," "Skeletor" and "Forrest Gump."

2. Ian Desmond's nicknames are "Desi" and "Charron."

3. "Chi Chi" is a nickname. Chi Chi Gonzalez's full name is Alexander Gonzalez.

4. "C.J." is a nickname. C.J. Cron's full name is Christopher John Cron.

5. Seth Smith goes by the nickname "Mr. Late Night".

6. Chris Iannetta goes by the nickname "Sponge."

7. Jason Giambi goes by the nickname "Giambino."

8. Chad Bettis goes by the nickname "Betty."

9. Tyler Chatwood goes by the nickname "Chatty."

10. Eric Young Sr. goes by the simple nickname "E.Y."

CHAPTER 5:

BOOGER

QUIZ TIME!

1. What is Larry Walker's full name?

    a. Ryan Larry Kristopher Walker

    b. Larry Kristopher Ryan Walker

    c. Larry Kenneth Robert Walker

    d. Kenneth Larry Robert Walker

2. Larry Walker played his entire 17-season MLB career with the Colorado Rockies.

    a. True

    b. False

3. Where was Larry Walker born?

    a. Branson, Missouri

    b. Walnut Creek, California

    c. Toronto, Canada

    d. Maple Ridge, Canada

4. When was Larry Walker born?

a. June 1, 1966

b. June 1, 1976

c. December 1, 1966

d. December 1, 1976

5. Larry Walker did NOT win a World Series championship.

a. True

b. False

6. How many All-Star Games was Larry Walker named to?

a. 2

b. 3

c. 4

d. 5

7. How many Silver Slugger Awards did Larry Walker win?

a. 1

b. 2

c. 3

d. 4

8. Larry Walker was inducted into the Canadian Sports Hall of Fame in 2007.

a. True

b. False

9. What year was Larry Walker inducted into the National Baseball Hall of Fame?

a. 2017

b. 2018

c. 2019

d. 2020

10. In how many seasons was Larry Walker the MLB batting champion?

    a. 1

    b. 2

    c. 3

    d. 4

11. What year did Larry Walker lead the National League in home runs?

    a. 1993

    b. 1995

    c. 1997

    d. 2001

12. Larry Walker was the first member of the National Baseball Hall of Fame to be depicted as a member of the Colorado Rockies on his plaque.

    a. True

    b. False

13. How many Gold Glove Awards did Larry Walker win?

    a. 2

    b. 4

    c. 5

    d. 7

14. Larry Walker was named the 1997 National League MVP.

a. True

b. False

15. How many home runs did Larry Walker hit?

    a. 243

    b. 283

    c. 343

    d. 383

16. How many at-bats did Larry Walker collect?

    a. 5,907

    b. 6,907

    c. 7,907

    d. 8,907

17. Larry Walker's career batting average was .313.

    a. True

    b. False

18. How many hits did Larry Walker collect?

    a. 1,960

    b. 2,060

    c. 2,160

    d. 2,260

19. How many bases did Larry Walker steal?

    a. 220

    b. 230

    c. 240

    d. 250

20. Larry Walker collected 1,311 RBIs.

    a. True

    b. False

QUIZ ANSWERS

1. C – Larry Kenneth Robert Walker
2. B – False (He played for the Colorado Rockies, Montreal Expos, and St. Louis Cardinals)
3. D – Maple Ridge, Canada
4. C – December 1, 1966
5. A – True
6. D – 5
7. C – 3
8. A – True
9. D – 2020
10. C – 3 (1998, 1999, 2001)
11. C – 1997
12. A – True
13. D – 7
14. A – True
15. D – 383
16. B – 6,907
17. A - True
18. C – 2,160
19. B – 230
20. A – True

DID YOU KNOW?

1. Larry Walker's career WAR is 72.7.

2. Larry Walker played 10 seasons with the Colorado Rockies, six seasons with the Montreal Expos, and two seasons with the St. Louis Cardinals.

3. Larry Walker was named the National League Player of the Month in April 1997 and July 2002. He was named the National League Player of the Week four times in his MLB career.

4. Larry Walker was inducted into the National Baseball Hall of Fame on his 10th and final ballot.

5. Larry Walker donated and helped open five Rockies Youth Field of Dreams facilities in Thornton, Northglenn, Denver, Aurora, and Fort Collins, Colorado.

6. Larry Walker loves bowling. He bowled a 300 game on April 10, 2014.

7. Since 2009, Larry Walker has coached for the Canadian national baseball team.

8. Larry Walker was named the 13th greatest Canadian sports figure in a 1999 edition of *Sports Illustrated.*

9. Larry Walker's No. 33 was set to be retired by the Colorado Rockies in 2020. Due to the COVID-19 pandemic, the uniform retirement date was pushed to 2021. The retirement

is now scheduled for September 25, before a game against the San Francisco Giants. He will join Todd Helton in having his number retired by the Rockies.

10. Larry Walker made his MLB debut at 22 years old in 1989 against the San Francisco Giants. He played his final game at 38 years old in 2005 against the Cincinnati Reds.

CHAPTER 6:

STATISTICALLY SPEAKING

QUIZ TIME!

1. Todd Helton holds the franchise record for the most home runs. How many did he hit during his MLB career?

    a. 349

    b. 359

    c. 369

    d. 379

2. Pitcher Jorge de la Rosa has the most wins in Colorado Rockies franchise history with 86.

    a. True

    b. False

3. Which pitcher holds the Colorado Rockies record for most career shutouts thrown with 3?

    a. Jason Jennings

    b. Ubaldo Jiménez

    c. Aaron Cook

    d. Both A and B

4. Which Colorado batter holds the single-season record for strikeouts with 191?

    a. Mark Reynolds
    b. Trevor Story
    c. Ian Desmond
    d. Ryan McMahon

5. Jorge de la Rosa has the most strikeouts in Colorado Rockies franchise history with how many?

    a. 965
    b. 975
    c. 985
    d. 995

6. Who has the most stolen bases in franchise history with 180?

    a. Carlos Gonzalez
    b. Larry Walker
    c. Charlie Blackmon
    d. Eric Young Sr.

7. Brian Fuentes holds the record for most saves in Colorado Rockies history with 115.

    a. True
    b. False

8. Who holds the Colorado Rockies record for being intentionally walked with 185?

    a. Larry Walker
    b. Todd Helton

c. Troy Tulowitzki

d. Nolan Arenado

9. Which two players are tied for the franchise record for home runs in a single season with 49 each?

   a. Andres Galarraga and Vinny Castilla

   b. Larry Walker and Nolan Arenado

   c. Todd Helton and Nolan Arenado

   d. Todd Helton and Larry Walker

10. Which batter holds the single-season Colorado Rockies record for hits with 219?

    a. Matt Holliday

    b. Ellis Burks

    c. Dante Bichette

    d. Juan Pierre

11. Which two players are tied for the single-season Colorado record for double plays grounded into with 27 each?

    a. Jay Payton and Charlie Hayes

    b. Jay Payton and Todd Zeile

    c. Todd Zeile and Charlie Hayes

    d. Garrett Atkins and Jay Payton

12. Todd Helton holds the record for the most sacrifice flies in Colorado franchise history with 93.

    a. True

    b. False

13. Jorge de la Rosa threw the most wild pitches in Colorado Rockies franchise history with how many?

a. 60

b. 70

c. 80

d. 90

14. Dexter Fowler holds the team's single-season record for most triples. How many did he hit in 2011?

    a. 5

    b. 10

    c. 15

    d. 20

15. Which hitter has the most walks in franchise history with 1,335?

    a. Carlos Gonzalez

    b. Troy Tulowitzki

    c. Larry Walker

    d. Todd Helton

16. Which hitter holds the time franchise record for best career batting average at .334?

    a. Dante Bichette

    b. Larry Walker

    c. Matt Holliday

    d. Andres Galarraga

17. Todd Helton holds the franchise record for most runs scored with 1,401.

    a. True

    b. False

18. Todd Helton has the most plate appearances in team history with how many?

    a. 9,453
    b. 10,453
    c. 11,453
    d. 12,453

19. Which pitcher holds the franchise record for most saves in a single season with 43?

    a. Jose Jiménez
    b. Huston Street
    c. Greg Holland
    d. Wade Davis

20. Aaron Cook holds the Colorado franchise record for most losses with 68.

    a. True
    b. False

QUIZ ANSWERS

1. C – 369

2. A - True

3. D – Both A and B

4. B – Trevor Story (2017)

5. C – 985

6. D – Eric Young Sr.

7. A – True

8. B – Todd Helton

9. D – Todd Helton (2001) and Larry Walker (1997)

10. C – Dante Bichette (1998)

11. B – Jay Payton (2003) and Todd Zeile (2002)

12. A – True

13. B – 70

14. C – 15

15. D – Todd Helton

16. B – Larry Walker

17. A – True

18. A – 9, 453

19. D – Wade Davis (2018)

20. A – True

DID YOU KNOW?

1. Aaron Cook threw the most innings in Colorado Rockies franchise history with 1,312.1. Coming in second is Jorge de la Rosa, who threw 1,141.1 innings.

2. Larry Walker had the best single-season batting average in Colorado Rockies franchise history at .379 in 1999. Coming in second is Todd Helton, who hit .372 in 2000.

3. Willy Taveras holds the Colorado Rockies franchise record for stolen base percentage with 86.33% success. Eric Young Sr. holds the franchise record for stolen bases with 180. Eric Young Sr. also holds the Colorado Rockies franchise record for the most times caught stealing at 69.

4. Todd Helton has the most extra-base hits in Colorado Rockies franchise history with 998. Second on the list is Larry Walker with 599.

5. Andres Galarraga holds the Colorado Rockies franchise record for at-bats per home run at 15.5. This means that, on average, Galarraga hit a home run about every 15 or 16 at-bats.

6. Jon Gray holds the franchise record for strikeouts per 9 innings pitched at 9.09. This means that, during his time with the Rockies, Gray recorded roughly 9 strikeouts in every 9 innings that he pitched.

7. Larry Walker holds the Colorado Rockies record for the most hit by pitches with 98. Pedro Astacio holds the team record for most batters hit with 58.

8. Todd Helton holds the Colorado Rockies franchise record for career doubles hit with 592. Second on the list is Larry Walker with 297.

9. Ubaldo Jiménez holds the Colorado Rockies single-season record for wins with 19 in 2010. Darryl Kile holds the team's single-season record for most losses with 17 in 1998.

10. German Marquez holds the franchise record for most strikeouts in a single season with 230 in 2018.

CHAPTER 7:

THE TRADE MARKET

QUIZ TIME!

1. On November 10, 2008, the Colorado Rockies traded Matt
    Holliday to which team in exchange for Carlos Gonzalez,
    Huston Street, and Greg Smith?

    a. San Diego Padres
    b. St. Louis Cardinals
    c. Oakland A's
    d. Los Angeles Angels of Anaheim

2. On July 28, 2015, the Colorado Rockies traded Troy
    Tulowitzki and LaTroy Hawkins to which team in exchange
    for Jose Reyes, Miguel Castro, Jeff Hoffman, and Jesus
    Tinoco?

    a. Los Angeles Dodgers
    b. Toronto Blue Jays
    c. New York Mets
    d. New York Yankees

3. The Colorado Rockies have made seven trades with the
    Arizona Diamondbacks.

a. True

b. False

4. On December 8, 2011, the Colorado Rockies traded Ian Stewart and Casey Weathers to which team in exchange for DJ LeMahieu and Tyler Colvin?

    a. Los Angeles Angels of Anaheim
    b. San Francisco Giants
    c. New York Yankees
    d. Chicago Cubs

5. The Colorado Rockies have made eight trades with the Milwaukee Brewers.

    a. True
    b. False

6. On November 17, 1992, the Colorado Rockies traded Kevin Reimer to which team in exchange for Dante Bichette?

    a. Boston Red Sox
    b. California Angels
    c. Milwaukee Brewers
    d. Cincinnati Reds

7. On April 30, 2008, the Colorado Rockies traded Ramon Ramirez to which team in exchange for Jorge de la Rosa?

    a. Milwaukee Brewers
    b. Kansas City Royals
    c. Arizona Diamondbacks
    d. Chicago Cubs

8. On December 16, 2001, the Colorado Rockies traded Jeff Cirillo to which team in exchange for Brian Fuentes, José Paniagua, and Denny Stark?

   a. Minnesota Twins
   b. San Diego Padres
   c. Milwaukee Brewers
   d. Seattle Mariners

9. On January 28, 2016, the Colorado Rockies traded Corey Dickerson and Kevin Padlo to which team in exchange for German Marquez and Jake McGee?

   a. Miami Marlins
   b. Tampa Bay Rays
   c. Pittsburgh Pirates
   d. Los Angeles Dodgers

10. The Colorado Rockies have made nine trades with the Miami Marlins.

    a. True
    b. False

11. On July 23, 2009, the Colorado Rockies Connor Graham to which team in exchange for Rafael Betancourt?

    a. Philadelphia Phillies
    b. Washington Nationals
    c. Cleveland Indians
    d. Boston Red Sox

12. The Colorado Rockies have made seven trades with the Seattle Mariners.

a. True

b. False

13. How many trades have the Colorado Rockies made with the Pittsburgh Pirates?

    a. 3

    b. 5

    c. 7

    d. 11

14. The Colorado Rockies have made six trades with the San Diego Padres.

    a. True

    b. False

15. On July 30, 2017, the Colorado Rockies traded Pedro Gonzalez to the Texas Rangers in exchange for whom?

    a. Dustin Garneau

    b. Ian Desmond

    c. Alexi Amarista

    d. Jonathan Lucroy

16. On November 16, 2002, the Colorado Rockies traded Juan Pierre, Mike Hampton, and cash considerations to which team in exchange for Vic Darensbourg, Pablo Ozuna, Charles Johnson, and Preston Wilson?

    a. Los Angeles Dodgers

    b. Chicago White Sox

    c. Florida Marlins

    d. Chicago Cubs

17. On July 30, 2011, the Colorado Rockies traded Ubaldo Jiménez to the which team in exchange for Matt McBride, Alex White, Joe Gardner and a player to be named later (Drew Pomeranz)?

    a. San Diego Padres
    b. Oakland A's
    c. Cleveland Indians
    d. Baltimore Orioles

18. On February 1, 2021, the Colorado Rockies traded Nolan Arenado to which team in exchange for Mateo Gil, Tony Locey, Elehuris Montero, Jake Sommers, and Austin Gomber?

    a. New York Yankees
    b. San Diego Padres
    c. Oakland A's
    d. St. Louis Cardinals

19. On December 13, 1999, the Colorado Rockies traded Vinny Castilla to which team in exchange for Rolando Arrojo and Aaron Ledesma?

    a. Atlanta Braves
    b. Tampa Bay Devil Rays
    c. Houston Astros
    d. Montreal Expos

20. The Colorado Rockies have made six trades with the Tampa Bay Rays.

    a. True
    b. False

QUIZ ANSWERS

1. C – Oakland A's

2. B – Toronto Blue Jays

3. A – True

4. D – Chicago Cubs

5. A – True

6. C – Milwaukee Brewers

7. B – Kansas City Royals

8. D – Seattle Mariners

9. B – Tampa Bay Rays

10. A – True

11. C – Cleveland Indians

12. A – True

13. B – 5

14. A – True

15. D – Jonathan Lucroy

16. C – Florida Marlins

17. C – Cleveland Indians

18. D – St. Louis Cardinals

19. B – Tampa Bay Devil Rays

20. A – True

DID YOU KNOW?

1. On August 6, 2004, the Colorado Rockies traded Larry Walker to the St. Louis Cardinals in exchange for Jason Burch and a player to be named later (Luiz Martinez and Chris Narveson).

2. On July 13, 2005, the Colorado Rockies traded Joe Kennedy and Jay Witasick to the Oakland A's in exchange for Eric Byrnes and Omar Quintanilla.

3. On November 20, 1995, the Colorado Rockies traded Joe Girardi to the New York Yankees in exchange for Mike DeJean.

4. On August 19, 1997, the Colorado Rockies traded Eric Young Sr. to the Los Angeles Dodgers in exchange for Pedro Astacio.

5. On July 31, 1998, the Colorado Rockies traded Ellis Burks to the San Francisco Giants in exchange for Darryl Hamilton, Jim Stoops, and a player to be named later (Jason Brester).

6. On January 16, 2012, the Colorado Rockies traded Seth Smith to the Oakland A's in exchange for Josh Outman and Guillermo Moscoso.

7. The Colorado Rockies have made four trades with the Atlanta Braves.

8. The Colorado Rockies have made four trades with the Detroit Tigers.

9. The Colorado Rockies have made five trades with the Los Angeles Angels.

10. The Colorado Rockies have made four trades with the San Francisco Giants.

CHAPTER 8:

DRAFT DAY

QUIZ TIME!

1. With which pick in the first round of the 1995 MLB draft did the Colorado Rockies select Todd Helton?

    a. 2nd

    b. 4th

    c. 8th

    d. 10th

2. With which pick in the first round of the 2005 MLB draft did the Colorado Rockies select Troy Tulowitzki?

    a. 2nd

    b. 4th

    c. 5th

    d. 7th

3. With which pick in the first round of the 2011 MLB draft did the Colorado Rockies select Trevor Story?

    a. 35th

    b. 40th

c. 45th

d. 50th

4. Nolan Arenado was drafted by the Colorado Rockies in which round of the 2009 MLB draft?

   a. 2nd

   b. 3rd

   c. 4th

   d. 5th

5. In which round of the 2008 MLB draft did the Colorado Rockies select Charlie Blackmon?

   a. 2nd

   b. 3rd

   c. 10th

   d. 11th

6. Aaron Cook was drafted by the Colorado Rockies in the second round of the MLB draft in which year?

   a. 1994

   b. 1995

   c. 1996

   d. 1997

7. DJ LeMahieu was drafted by the Chicago Cubs in the second round of the 2009 MLB draft.

   a. True

   b. False

8. Jason Giambi was drafted by which team in the second round of the 1992 MLB draft?

a. Cleveland Indians

b. New York Yankees

c. Oakland A's

d. Milwaukee Brewers

9. Justin Morneau was drafted by which team in the third round of the 1999 MLB draft?

a. Colorado Rockies

b. Minnesota Twins

c. Pittsburgh Pirates

d. Chicago White Sox

10. Huston Street was drafted by the Oakland A's in the first round (40th overall) of the 2004 MLB draft.

a. True

b. False

11. Jason Hammel was drafted by which team in the 10th round of the 2002 MLB draft?

a. Chicago Cubs

b. Kansas City Royals

c. Baltimore Orioles

d. Tampa Bay Devil Rays

12. Seth Smith was drafted by the Colorado Rockies in the second round of the 2004 MLB draft.

a. True

b. False

13. Dexter Fowler was drafted by the Colorado Rockies in which round of the 2004 MLB draft?

a. 4th

b. 5th

c. 14th

d. 15th

14. Ryan Spilborghs was drafted by the Colorado Rockies in which round of the 2002 MLB draft?

a. 4th

b. 7th

c. 10th

d. 17th

15. Jeff Cirillo was drafted by which team in the 11th round of the 1991 MLB draft?

a. San Diego Padres

b. Arizona Diamondbacks

c. Seattle Mariners

d. Milwaukee Brewers

16. Juan Pierre was drafted by the Colorado Rockies in which round of the 1998 MLB draft?

a. 9th

b. 11th

c. 13th

d. 15th

17. Michael Cuddyer was drafted by which team in the first round (ninth overall) of the 1997 MLB draft?

a. Colorado Rockies

b. Florida Marlins

c. New York Mets

d. Minnesota Twins

18. Jamie Moyer was drafted by which team in the sixth round of the 1984 MLB draft?

a. Texas Rangers

b. Philadelphia Phillies

c. Chicago Cubs

d. Seattle Mariners

19. Joe Girardi was drafted by which team in the fifth round of the 1986 MLB draft?

a. St. Louis Cardinals

b. New York Yankees

c. Chicago Cubs

d. Philadelphia Phillies

20. Eric Young Sr. was drafted by the Los Angeles Dodgers in the 43rd round of the 1989 MLB draft.

a. True

b. False

QUIZ ANSWERS

1. C – 8th

2. D – 7th

3. C – 45th

4. A – 2nd

5. A – 2nd

6. D – 1997

7. A – True

8. C – Oakland A's

9. B – Minnesota Twins

10. A – True

11. D – Tampa Bay Devil Rays

12. A – True

13. C – 14th

14. B – 7th

15. D – Milwaukee Brewers

16. C – 13th

17. D – Minnesota Twins

18. C – Chicago Cubs

19. C – Chicago Cubs

20. A – True

DID YOU KNOW?

1. Eric Byrnes was drafted in the eighth round of the 1998 MLB draft by the Oakland A's.

2. Walt Weiss was drafted in the first round (11th overall) in the 1985 MLB draft by the Oakland A's.

3. Craig Counsell was drafted in the 11th round of the 1992 MLB draft by the Colorado Rockies.

4. John Vander Wal was drafted in the third round of the 1987 MLB draft by the Montreal Expos.

5. Bret Saberhagen was drafted in the 19th round of the 1982 MLB draft by the Kansas City Royals.

6. Dante Bichette was drafted in the 17th round of the 1984 MLB draft by the California Angels.

7. Ellis Burks was drafted in the first round (20th overall) of the 1983 MLB draft by the Boston Red Sox.

8. Mark Reynolds was drafted in the 16th round of the 2004 MLB draft by the Arizona Diamondbacks.

9. Ian Desmond was drafted in the third round of the 2004 MLB draft by the Montreal Expos.

10. Chris Iannetta was drafted in the fourth round of the 2004 MLB draft by the Colorado Rockies.

CHAPTER 9:

ODDS AND ENDS

QUIZ TIME!

1. Jamie Moyer and his ex-wife, Karen, were introduced by which famous baseball broadcaster?

   a. Vin Scully
   b. Bob Uecker
   c. Harry Caray
   d. Tim McCarver

2. Jason Giambi's brother, Jeremy, also played MLB.

   a. True
   b. False

3. Yonder Alonso's brother-in-law also plays MLB. Who is his brother-in-law?

   a. Bryce Harper
   b. Kris Bryant
   c. Manny Machado
   d. Clayton Kershaw

4. In 2019, Eric Byrnes set the Guinness world record for doing what?

   a. Fastest 100-meter hurdles wearing swim fins
   b. Most holes of golf in a single day
   c. Most pull-ups in 24 hours
   d. Fastest 50 meters walking on hands with soccer ball between the legs

5. What college did Bud Black attend and receive a bachelor's degree in management from?

   a. Oregon State University
   b. Colorado State University
   c. Long Beach State University
   d. San Diego State University

6. LaTroy Hawkins is the godfather of which current NFL quarterback?

   a. Russell Wilson
   b. Patrick Mahomes
   c. Aaron Rodgers
   d. Kirk Cousins

7. Ellis Burks is a cousin of fellow former MLB outfielder Roosevelt Brown.

   a. True
   b. False

8. Michael Cuddyer has been deaf in his left ear since he was 11 years old.

a. True

b. False

9. Which MLB team was Trevor Story a fan of while he was growing up?

   a. Texas Rangers

   b. Houston Astros

   c. Oakland A's

   d. New York Yankees

10. Jeff Cirillo is currently an MLB scout for which MLB team?

    a. Miami Marlins

    b. Los Angeles Angels

    c. Arizona Diamondbacks

    d. San Diego Padres

11. In his entire high school career, Aaron Cook gave up only one home run. Which fellow future MLB player did Cook give up the home run to?

    a. Jim Thome

    b. Derek Jeter

    c. Johnny Damon

    d. Kevin Youkilis

12. Ubaldo Jiménez threw a no-hitter as a member of the Colorado Rockies on April 17, 2010.

    a. True

    b. False

13. Jonathan Lucroy played for which team in the 2017 World Baseball Classic?

    a. Canada
    b. Netherlands
    c. Italy
    d. USA

14. DJ LeMahieu is the first MLB player in the modern era to win a batting title in each league.

    a. True
    b. False

15. Which MLB team was Charlie Blackmon a fan of while he was growing up?

    a. Houston Astros
    b. Los Angeles Dodgers
    c. Atlanta Braves
    d. Texas Rangers

16. Nolan Arenado and Josh Fuentes are cousins.

    a. True
    b. False

17. Who was Matt Holliday's favorite baseball player while he was growing up?

    a. Rickey Henderson
    b. Cal Ripken Jr.
    c. Tony Gwynn
    d. Mark McGwire

18. Which MLB team was Charlie Culberson a fan of while he was growing up?

    a. Florida Marlins
    b. Kansas City Royals
    c. Atlanta Braves
    d. California Angels

19. Which two former Rockies are currently coaches with the Atlanta Braves?

    a. Eric Young Sr. and Larry Walker
    b. Walt Weiss and Larry Walker
    c. Walt Weiss and Eric Young Sr.
    d. Ellis Burks and Walt Weiss

20. C.J. Cron's dad, Chris Cron, also played in the MLB. So did his cousin, Chad Moeller.

    a. True
    b. False

QUIZ ANSWERS

1. C – Harry Caray

2. A – True

3. C – Manny Machado

4. B – Most holes of golf in a single day (420 holes)

5. D – San Diego State University

6. B – Patrick Mahomes, Kansas City Chiefs

7. A – True

8. A – True

9. A – Texas Rangers

10. B – Los Angeles Angels

11. D – Kevin Youkilis

12. A – True

13. D – USA

14. A – True

15. C – Atlanta Braves

16. A – True

17. B – Cal Ripken Jr.

18. C – Atlanta Braves

19. C – Walt Weiss and Eric Young Sr.

20. A – True

DID YOU KNOW?

1. Current San Francisco Giants manager Gabe Kapler is only the seventh Jewish manager in MLB history. He went to the same high school as Ice Cube. Kapler played for the Rockies in 2002 and 2003.

2. Bo Bichette is named after Bo Jackson. Bichette is the son of Dante Bichette, who is now a member of the Toronto Blue Jays organization.

3. Jose Reyes was the cover athlete for the video game Major League Baseball 2K8 by 2K Sports.

4. Jon Gray does ghost hunting in hotels with ghost-hunting equipment. This is something he has been doing since he was 10 years old.

5. Dexter Fowler was a member of the 2008 United States National Baseball team, which won a bronze medal in the 2008 Summer Olympics.

6. Drew Pomeranz is the great-grandson of professional baseball/professional football player Garland Buckeye.

7. When Ian Desmond's first child was born, he became one of the first players in MLB history to take paternity leave.

8. In June 2014, Daniel Murphy was invited to speak at the White House during the Working Families Summit.

9. Jay Payton is currently a college baseball in-game analyst for ESPNU.

10. John Axford has a bachelor's degree in film and television from Notre Dame.

CHAPTER 10:

OUTFIELDERS

QUIZ TIME!

1. How many All-Star Games was Dante Bichette named to during his 14-season MLB career?

   a. 2

   b. 4

   c. 6

   d. 8

2. Ellis Burks won two Silver Slugger Awards in his 18-season MLB career.

   a. True

   b. False

3. What year was Larry Walker inducted into the National Baseball Hall of Fame?

   a. 2017

   b. 2018

   c. 2019

   d. 2020

4. Brad Hawpe spent his entire nine-season career with the Colorado Rockies.

   a. True

   b. False

5. How many All-Star Games was Matt Holliday named to in his 15-season MLB career?

   a. 1

   b. 3

   c. 7

   d. 9

6. How many Silver Slugger Awards has Charlie Blackmon won?

   a. 1

   b. 2

   c. 3

   d. 4

7. During his 12-season MLB career, Carlos Gonzalez won three Gold Glove Awards.

   a. True

   b. False

8. In his 15-season MLB career, Michael Cuddyer played for the Colorado Rockies, New York Mets, and which other franchise?

   a. Los Angeles Dodgers

   b. Texas Rangers

c. Baltimore Orioles

d. Minnesota Twins

9. How many seasons did Juan Pierre spend with the Colorado Rockies?

   a. 2

   b. 3

   c. 4

   d. 5

10. How many seasons did Dexter Fowler spend with the Colorado Rockies?

    a. 1

    b. 4

    c. 6

    d. 8

11. During his 11-season MLB career, Seth Smith played for the Colorado Rockies, Seattle Mariners, San Diego Padres, Baltimore Orioles, and which other team?

    a. Los Angeles Dodgers

    b. Oakland A's

    c. Washington Nationals

    d. Miami Marlins

12. Ryan Spilborghs spent his entire seven-season MLB career with the Colorado Rockies.

    a. True

    b. False

13. Gerardo Parra won a World Series championship with the Washington Nationals in which season?

    a. 2017
    b. 2018
    c. 2019
    d. 2020

14. In his 13-season MLB career, Darryl Hamilton played for the Colorado Rockies, New York Mets, San Francisco Giants, Texas Rangers, and which other team?

    a. Houston Astros
    b. Cincinnati Reds
    c. Detroit Tigers
    d. Milwaukee Brewers

15. How many seasons did Jay Payton spend with the Colorado Rockies?

    a. 1
    b. 2
    c. 3
    d. 4

16. Gabe Kapler is the current manager of which MLB team?

    a. Boston Red Sox
    b. San Francisco Giants
    c. Tampa Bay Rays
    d. Detroit Tigers

17. How many All-Star Games was Jeromy Burnitz named to in his 14-season MLB career?

a. 1

b. 2

c. 4

d. 5

18. How many seasons did Corey Dickerson spend with the Colorado Rockies?

a. 1

b. 2

c. 3

d. 4

19. How many Silver Slugger Awards did Eric Young Sr. win during his 15-season MLB career?

a. 1

b. 2

c. 3

d. 4

20. Ian Desmond has won three Silver Slugger Awards.

a. True

b. False

QUIZ ANSWERS

1. B – 4
2. A – True
3. D – 2020
4. B – False (He also played for the San Diego Padres, Los Angeles Angels, and Tampa Bay Rays.)
5. C – 7
6. B – 2
7. A – True
8. D – Minnesota Twins
9. B – 3
10. C – 6
11. B – Oakland A's
12. A – True
13. C – 2019
14. D – Milwaukee Brewers
15. C – 3
16. B – San Francisco Giants
17. A – 1
18. C – 3
19. A – 1
20. A – True

DID YOU KNOW?

1. Larry Walker spent 10 seasons of his MLB career with the Colorado Rockies. He also played for the Montreal Expos and St. Louis Cardinals. He is a member of the National Baseball Hall of Fame, the 1997 National League MVP, a five-time All-Star, seven-time Gold Glove Award winner, three-time Silver Slugger Award winner, and three-time batting champion.

2. Ellis Burks spent five seasons of his MLB career with the Colorado Rockies. He also played for the Boston Red Sox, Cleveland Indians, San Francisco Giants, and Chicago White Sox. He is a two-time All-Star, two-time Silver Slugger Award winner, and a Gold Glove Award winner in 1990.

3. Dante Bichette spent seven seasons of his MLB career with the Colorado Rockies. He also played for the California Angels, Boston Red Sox, Milwaukee Brewers, and Cincinnati Reds. He is a four-time All-Star and a Silver Slugger Award winner in 1995.

4. Matt Holliday spent six seasons of his MLB career with the Colorado Rockies. He also played for the St. Louis Cardinals, Oakland A's, and New York Yankees. He is a seven-time All-Star, four-time Silver Slugger Award winner, the 2007 National League batting champion, the 2007 NLCS MVP, and 2011 World Series champion.

5. Carlos Gonzalez spent 10 seasons of his MLB career with the Colorado Rockies. He also played for the Oakland A's, Cleveland Indians, and Chicago Cubs. He is a three-time All-Star, two-time Silver Slugger Award winner, three-time Gold Glove Award winner, and the 2010 National League batting champion.

6. Charlie Blackmon currently plays for the Colorado Rockies. He has been with the team since 2011. He is a four-time All-Star, two-time Silver Slugger Award winner, and the 2017 National League batting champion.

7. Michael Cuddyer spent three seasons of his MLB career with the Colorado Rockies. He also played for the Minnesota Twins and New York Mets. He is a two-time All-Star, a 2013 Silver Slugger Award winner, and 2013 National League batting champion.

8. Eric Young Sr. spent five seasons of his MLB career with the Colorado Rockies. He also played for the Los Angeles Dodgers, Texas Rangers, San Diego Padres, Chicago Cubs, Milwaukee Brewers, and San Francisco Giants. He was named to the All-Star Game in 1996, the same year he won his only Silver Slugger Award.

9. Dexter Fowler spent six seasons of his MLB career with the Colorado Rockies. He also played for the St. Louis Cardinals, Chicago Cubs, Los Angeles Angels, and Houston Astros. He was named an All-Star in 2016 and is a 2016 World Series champion.

10. Ian Desmond has spent three seasons of his MLB career with the Colorado Rockies. He also played for the Washington Nationals and Texas Rangers. He is a two-time All-Star and three-time Silver Slugger Award winner.

CHAPTER 11:

INFIELDERS

QUIZ TIME!

1. How many All-Star Games was Troy Tulowitzki named to during his 13-season MLB career?

    a. 1

    b. 3

    c. 5

    d. 7

2. Todd Helton spent his entire 17-season MLB career with the Colorado Rockies.

    a. True

    b. False

3. How many Gold Glove Awards has Nolan Arenado won?

    a. 2

    b. 4

    c. 6

    d. 8

4. How many Silver Slugger Awards has Trevor Story won?

a. 0

b. 1

c. 2

d. 3

5. How many Silver Slugger Awards did Vinny Castilla win in his 16-season MLB career?

    a. 1

    b. 2

    c. 3

    d. 4

6. How many Gold Glove Awards has DJ LeMahieu won?

    a. 1

    b. 3

    c. 4

    d. 6

7. Walt Weiss was named the 1988 American League Rookie of the Year.

    a. True

    b. False

8. How many All-Star Games was Andres Galarraga named during his 19-season MLB career?

    a. 2

    b. 3

    c. 5

    d. 6

9. How many seasons did Clint Barmes spend with the Colorado Rockies?

    a. 2
    b. 4
    c. 6
    d. 8

10. During his 20-season MLB career, Jason Giambi played for the Colorado Rockies, Oakland A's, Cleveland Indians, and which other team?

    a. Texas Rangers
    b. New York Yankees
    c. New York Mets
    d. Boston Red Sox

11. How many seasons did Eric Young Jr. spend with the Colorado Rockies?

    a. 1
    b. 3
    c. 5
    d. 7

12. Neifi Pérez spent six seasons of his MLB career with the Colorado Rockies.

    a. True
    b. False

13. How many All-Star Games was Melvin Mora named to in his 13-season MLB career?

a. 1

b. 2

c. 3

d. 4

14. Craig Counsell is currently the manager of which MLB team?

    a. Miami Marlins

    b. Los Angeles Dodgers

    c. Arizona Diamondbacks

    d. Milwaukee Brewers

15. Jamey Carroll played for the Colorado Rockies, Minnesota Twins, Los Angeles Dodgers, Cleveland Indians, Kansas City Royals, and which other franchise?

    a. Texas Rangers

    b. Tampa Bay Rays

    c. San Francisco Giants

    d. Washington Nationals

16. Justin Morneau was named the 2014 National League MVP.

    a. True

    b. False

17. How many All-Star Games was Marco Scutaro named to during his 13-season MLB career?

    a. 0

    b. 1

    c. 2

    d. 3

18. How many World Series championships did Juan Uribe win in his 16-season MLB career?

    a. 0
    b. 1
    c. 2
    d. 3

19. How many seasons did Garrett Atkins spend with the Colorado Rockies?

    a. 1
    b. 3
    c. 5
    d. 7

20. Ty Wigginton was named to one All-Star Game.

    a. True
    b. False

QUIZ ANSWERS

1. C – 5

2. A – True

3. D – 8

4. C – 2

5. C – 3

6. B – 3

7. A – True

8. C – 5

9. D – 8

10. B – New York Yankees

11. C – 5

12. A – True

13. B – 2

14. D – Milwaukee Brewers

15. D – Washington Nationals

16. B – False (He finished in 23rd place.)

17. B – 1

18. C – 2

19. D – 7

20. A – True

DID YOU KNOW?

1. Todd Helton spent his entire 17-season MLB career with the Colorado Rockies. He is a five-time All-Star, three-time Gold Glove Award winner, four-time Silver Slugger Award winner, and the 2000 batting champion.

2. Troy Tulowitzki spent 10 seasons of his MLB career with the Colorado Rockies. He also played for the Toronto Blue Jays and New York Yankees. He is a five-time All-Star, two-time Silver Slugger Award winner, and two-time Gold Glove Award winner.

3. Nolan Arenado spent eight seasons of his MLB career with the Colorado Rockies. He currently plays for the St. Louis Cardinals. So far in his career, he is a five-time All-Star, eight-time Gold Glove Award winner, four-time Platinum Glove winner, and four-time Silver Slugger Award winner.

4. Trevor Story currently plays for the Colorado Rockies. He has been with the team since 2016. So far in his career, he is a two-time All-Star and two-time Silver Slugger Award winner.

5. Vinny Castilla spent nine seasons of his MLB career with the Colorado Rockies. He also played for the Atlanta Braves, Tampa Bay Devil Rays, San Diego Padres, Washington Nationals, and Houston Astros. He is a two-time All-Star and three-time Silver Slugger Award winner.

6. DJ LeMahieu spent seven seasons of his MLB career with the Colorado Rockies. He currently plays for the New York Yankees. He has also played for the Chicago Cubs. So far in his MLB career, he is a three-time All-Star, three-time Gold Glove Award winner, two-time Silver Slugger Award winner, and two-time batting champion.

7. Walt Weiss spent four seasons of his MLB career with the Colorado Rockies. He also played for the Oakland A's, Atlanta Braves, and Florida Marlins. He was an All-Star in 1998, 1989 World Series champion, and 1988 American League Rookie of the Year. He was the Rockies' manager from 2013 to 2016.

8. Andres Galarraga spent five seasons of his MLB career with the Colorado Rockies. He also played for the Montreal Expos, San Francisco Giants, Atlanta Braves, Texas Rangers, Anaheim Angels, and St. Louis Cardinals. He is a five-time All-Star, two-time Gold Glove Award winner, two-time Silver Slugger Award winner, and the 1993 National League batting champion.

9. Jason Giambi spent four seasons of his MLB career with the Colorado Rockies. He also played for the Oakland A's, New York Yankees, and Cleveland Indians. He was the 2000 American League MVP, a five-time All-Star, and a two-time Silver Slugger Award winner.

10. Justin Morneau spent two seasons of his MLB career with the Colorado Rockies. He also played for the Minnesota Twins, Pittsburgh Pirates, and Chicago White Sox. He was

the 2006 American League MVP, a four-time All-Star, two-time Silver Slugger Award winner, and 2014 National League batting champion.

CHAPTER 12:

PITCHERS AND CATCHERS

QUIZ TIME!

1. How many All-Star Games was Ubaldo Jiménez named to during his 12-season MLB career?

    a. 0

    b. 1

    c. 2

    d. 3

2. Aaron Cook spent his entire 11-season MLB career with the Colorado Rockies.

    a. True

    b. False

3. How many World Series championships did Joe Girardi win during his 15-season MLB career?

    a. 1

    b. 2

    c. 3

    d. 4

4. How many seasons did Jorge de la Rosa spend with the Colorado Rockies?

   a. 3
   b. 6
   c. 8
   d. 9

5. In his 14-season MLB career, Chris Iannetta played for the Colorado Rockies, Arizona Diamondbacks, Seattle Mariners, and which other franchise?

   a. Los Angeles Angels
   b. Los Angeles Dodgers
   c. Miami Marlins
   d. Washington Nationals

6. How many All-Star Games was Brian Fuentes named to in his 12-season MLB career?

   a. 1
   b. 2
   c. 3
   d. 4

7. Huston Street was named the 2005 American League Rookie of the Year.

   a. True
   b. False

8. How many Cy Young Awards did Bret Saberhagen win during his 16-season MLB career?

a. 1

b. 2

c. 3

d. 4

9. How many All-Star Games was Darryl Kile named to during his 12-season MLB career?

a. 1

b. 2

c. 3

d. 4

10. How many All-Star Games has Wade Davis been named to?

a. 1

b. 2

c. 3

d. 4

11. How many seasons did Jeff Francis spend with the Colorado Rockies?

a. 2

b. 4

c. 6

d. 8

12. Jamie Moyer pitched in the major leagues for 25 seasons.

a. True

b. False

13. During his 13-season MLB career, Jason Hammel played for the Colorado Rockies, Chicago Cubs, Kansas City Royals, Baltimore Orioles, Oakland A's, and which other team?

    a. Tampa Bay Rays
    b. Boston Red Sox
    c. Los Angeles Angels
    d. San Diego Padres

14. John Axford was named the National League Rolaids Relief Pitcher of the Year in which season?

    a. 2009
    b. 2010
    c. 2011
    d. 2012

15. How many All-Star Games has Drew Pomeranz been named to?

    a. 0
    b. 1
    c. 2
    d. 3

16. LaTroy Hawkins spent three seasons of his 21-season MLB career with the Colorado Rockies.

    a. True
    b. False

17. How many Gold Glove Awards did Kirt Manwaring win during his 13-season MLB career?

a. 0

b. 1

c. 2

d. 3

18. How many seasons did Yorvit Torrealba spend with the Colorado Rockies?

    a. 2

    b. 3

    c. 4

    d. 5

19. Jon Gray made his MLB debut with the Colorado Rockies in what year?

    a. 2013

    b. 2014

    c. 2015

    d. 2016

20. Chad Bettis spent his entire seven-season MLB career with the Colorado Rockies.

    a. True

    b. False

QUIZ ANSWERS

1. B – 1

2. B – False (He spent 10 seasons with the Rockies and one season with the Boston Red Sox.)

3. C – 3

4. D – 9

5. A – Los Angeles Angels

6. D – 4

7. A – True

8. B – 2

9. C – 3

10. C – 3

11. D – 8

12. A – True

13. A – Tampa Bay Rays

14. C – 2011

15. B – 1

16. A – True

17. B – 1

18. D – 5

19. C – 2015

20. A – True

DID YOU KNOW?

1. Ubaldo Jiménez spent six seasons of his MLB career with the Colorado Rockies. He also played for the Cleveland Indians and Baltimore Orioles. He was named an All-Star in 2010.

2. Aaron Cook spent 10 seasons of his MLB career with the Colorado Rockies. He also played for the Boston Red Sox. He was named an All-Star in 2008.

3. Joe Girardi spent three seasons of his MLB career with the Colorado Rockies. He also played for the New York Yankees, Chicago Cubs, and St. Louis Cardinals. He was an All-Star in 2000, a three-time World Series champion, and the 2006 National League Manager of the Year Award winner. He was the manager of the Florida Marlins for the 2006 season and managed the New York Yankees from 2008 through 2017. He has been the manager of the Philadelphia Phillies since the 2020 season.

4. Huston Street spent three seasons of his MLB career with the Colorado Rockies. He also played for the Los Angeles Angels, San Diego Padres, and Oakland A's. He is a two-time All-Star and the 2005 American League Rookie of the Year.

5. Darryl Kile spent two seasons of his MLB career with the Colorado Rockies. He also played for the Houston Astros and St. Louis Cardinals. He is a three-time All-Star.

6. Wade Davis spent three seasons of his MLB career with the Colorado Rockies. He currently plays for the Kansas City Royals. He has also played for the Tampa Bay Rays and Chicago Cubs. So far in his career, he is a three-time All-Star and a 2015 World Series Champion.

7. Jamie Moyer played the 2012 season with the Colorado Rockies. He also played for the Seattle Mariners, Philadelphia Phillies, Chicago Cubs, Baltimore Orioles, Texas Rangers, St. Louis Cardinals, and Boston Red Sox. He was an All-Star in 2003 and a 2008 World Series champion.

8. Kirt Manwaring spent three seasons of his MLB career with the Colorado Rockies. He also played for the San Francisco Giants and Houston Astros. He won a Gold Glove Award in 1993.

9. Bret Saberhagen appeared in 9 games for the Colorado Rockies during the 1995 season. He also played for the Kansas City Royals, New York Mets, and Boston Red Sox. He is a two-time Cy Young Award winner, three-time All-Star, 1989 Gold Glove Award winner, the American League ERA leader in 1995, 1985 World Series champion, and 1985 World Series MVP.

10. Brian Fuentes spent seven seasons of his MLB career with the Colorado Rockies. He also played for the Oakland A's, Los Angeles Angels, Minnesota Twins, St. Louis Cardinals, and Seattle Mariners. He is a four-time All-Star.

CHAPTER 13:

WORLD SERIES

QUIZ TIME!

1. How many World Series championships have the Colorado Rockies won?

   a. 0
   b. 1
   c. 2
   d. 3

2. How many NL pennants have the Colorado Rockies won?

   a. 0
   b. 1
   c. 2
   d. 3

3. How many wild card berths have the Colorado Rockies earned?

   a. 1
   b. 3
   c. 5
   d. 7

4. Which team did the Colorado Rockies face in the 2007 World Series?

    a. Los Angeles Angels of Anaheim
    b. Cleveland Indians
    c. New York Yankees
    d. Boston Red Sox

5. How many games did the 2007 World Series go?

    a. 4
    b. 5
    c. 6
    d. 7

6. Who was Colorado's starting pitcher in Game 1 of the 2007 World Series?

    a. Josh Fogg
    b. Aaron Cook
    c. Ubaldo Jiménez
    d. Jeff Francis

7. The 2007 World Series took place from October 24 through October 28.

    a. True
    b. False

8. Which Colorado Rockies batter did NOT hit a home run in the 2007 World Series?

    a. Garrett Atkins
    b. Troy Tulowitzki

c. Brad Hawpe

d. Matt Holliday

9. Which Colorado Rockies batter had the most RBIs in the 2007 World Series?

a. Garrett Atkins

b. Troy Tulowitzki

c. Brad Hawpe

d. Matt Holliday

10. Which Colorado Rockies batter had the most at-bats in the 2007 World Series?

a. Kazuo Matsui

b. Matt Holliday

c. Todd Helton

d. Both A and B

11. Which Colorado Rockies pitcher did NOT record a loss during the 2007 World Series?

a. Aaron Cook

b. Jeff Francis

c. LaTroy Hawkins

d. Ubaldo Jiménez

12. Of all Colorado Rockies pitchers, Franklin Morales allowed the most earned runs during the 2007 World Series with 7.

a. True

b. False

13. Which Colorado pitcher recorded the most strikeouts in the 2007 World Series?

    a. Jeff Francis

    b. Matt Herges

    c. Jeremy Affeldt

    d. Aaron Cook

14. Which Rockies pitcher gave up the most walks in the 2007 World Series?

    a. Ryan Speier

    b. Jeff Francis

    c. Josh Fogg

    d. Ubaldo Jiménez

15. Which Colorado Rockies pitcher pitched the most innings in the 2007 World Series?

    a. Aaron Cook

    b. Jeff Francis

    c. Ubaldo Jiménez

    d. Brian Fuentes

16. The Rockies faced the Arizona Diamondbacks in the 2007 National League Championship Series.

    a. True

    b. False

17. Who was manager of the Colorado Rockies in the 2007 World Series?

    a. Don Baylor

    b. Jim Tracy

c. Clint Hurdle

d. Walt Weiss

18. Which team did the Colorado Rockies face in the 2007 National League Division Series?

    a. Los Angeles Dodgers

    b. Chicago Cubs

    c. Philadelphia Phillies

    d. New York Mets

19. Which Colorado Rockies batter was walked the most in the 2007 World Series?

    a. Todd Helton

    b. Garrett Atkins

    c. Ryan Spilborghs

    d. Troy Tulowitzki

20. Todd Helton had a .333 batting average in the 2007 World Series.

    a. True

    b. False

QUIZ ANSWERS

1. A – 0

2. B – 1

3. C – 5

4. D – Boston Red Sox

5. A – 4

6. D – Jeff Francis

7. A – True

8. B – Troy Tulowitzki

9. D – Matt Holliday (3)

10. D – Both A and B (17 each)

11. C – LaTroy Hawkins

12. A - True

13. B – Matt Herges (4)

14. D – Ubaldo Jiménez (5)

15. A – Aaron Cook (6.0)

16. A – True

17. C – Clint Hurdle

18. C – Philadelphia Phillies

19. B – Garrett Atkins (3)

20. A – True

DID YOU KNOW?

1. Mike Lowell was named the 2007 World Series MVP. Matt Holliday was named the 2007 NLCS MVP.

2. Josh Fogg and Jeff Francis each gave up 10 hits, tied for the most hits given up by Colorado Rockies pitchers in the 2007 World Series.

3. Josh Fogg's ERA in the 2007 World Series was 20.25.

4. Todd Helton, Matt Holliday, and Kazuo Matsui each had 5 hits, tied for the most hits by Colorado Rockies batters in the 2007 World Series.

5. Jeremy Affeldt, Garrett Atkins, Brad Hawpe, Todd Helton, Matt Holliday, Kazuo Matsui, Ryan Spilborghs, Yorvit Torrealba, and Troy Tulowitzki each played in all 4 games of the 2007 World Series.

6. The Colorado Rockies became the first National League team to get swept in a World Series after sweeping in the NLCS.

7. To this day, the 2007 World Series remains the Colorado Rockies' only World Series appearance.

8. Games 1 and 2 of the 2007 World Series took place at Fenway Park. Games 3 and 4 took place at Coors Field.

9. Game 1 of the 2007 World Series featured Ashanti singing *God Bless America*. Game 2 of the 2007 World Series

featured James Taylor singing the National Anthem and Boyz II Men singing *God Bless America*. Game 3 of the 2007 World Series featured Carrie Underwood singing the National Anthem and Philip Bailey of the band *Earth Wind and Fire* singing *God Bless America*. Game 4 of the 2007 World Series featured Trisha Yearwood singing the National Anthem and Lonestar singing *God Bless America*.

10. The Colorado Rockies entered the 2007 World Series having won 21 of their last 22 games.

CHAPTER 14:

HEATED RIVALRIES

QUIZ TIME!

1. Which team does NOT play in the National League West with the Colorado Rockies?

   a. Arizona Diamondbacks
   b. San Diego Padres
   c. Los Angeles Dodgers
   d. Oakland A's

2. The Atlanta Braves were in the National League West Division from 1969 to 1993.

   a. True
   b. False

3. Which team was a member of the NL West Division from 1969-1993?

   a. Florida Marlins
   b. Milwaukee Brewers
   c. Cincinnati Reds
   d. Chicago Cubs

4. What current National League West team has the most NL West championships?

    a. San Francisco Giants
    b. Los Angeles Dodgers
    c. San Diego Padres
    d. Arizona Diamondbacks

5. The Houston Astros were members of the National League West from 1969-1993.

    a. True
    b. False

6. Which team won the National League West in 2020?

    a. Colorado Rockies
    b. San Francisco Giants
    c. San Diego Padres
    d. Los Angeles Dodgers

7. The Colorado Rockies have never won an NL West Division championship.

    a. True
    b. False

8. The Colorado Rockies have not won any World Series championships. How many have the Los Angeles Dodgers won?

    a. 5
    b. 7
    c. 9
    d. 12

9. The Colorado Rockies have not won any World Series championships. How many have the San Diego Padres won?

   a. 0
   b. 1
   c. 2
   d. 3

10. The Colorado Rockies have not won any World Series championships. How many have the San Francisco Giants won?

    a. 2
    b. 4
    c. 6
    d. 8

11. The Colorado Rockies have not won any World Series championships. How many have the Arizona Diamond-backs won?

    a. 0
    b. 1
    c. 2
    d. 3

12. The Colorado Rockies were members of the American League West Division from 1993 to 2000.

    a. True
    b. False

13. Which player has NOT played for both the Colorado Rockies and the Los Angeles Dodgers?

    a. Troy Tulowitzki
    b. Craig Counsell
    c. Eric Young Sr.
    d. Charlie Culberson

14. Which player has NOT played for both the Colorado Rockies and the San Diego Padres?

    a. Jhoulys Chacin
    b. Jeff Cirillo
    c. DJ LeMahieu
    d. Seth Smith

15. Which player has NOT played for both the Colorado Rockies and the San Francisco Giants?

    a. Andres Galarraga
    b. Marco Scutaro
    c. Jeremy Affeldt
    d. Vinny Castilla

16. The National League West Division was formed in 1969.

    a. True
    b. False

17. Which player has NOT played for both the Colorado Rockies and the Arizona Diamondbacks?

    a. Eric Byrnes
    b. Jamey Carroll

c. Chris Iannetta

d. Jorge de la Rosa

18. How many National League West Division titles did the Cincinnati Reds win before they moved to the NL Central Division?

    a. 0

    b. 2

    c. 5

    d. 7

19. How many National League West Division titles did the Atlanta Braves win before they moved to the NL East Division?

    a. 0

    b. 1

    c. 3

    d. 5

20. The Houston Astros won two National League West Division championships before they moved to the NL Central Division.

    a. True

    b. False

QUIZ ANSWERS

1. D – Oakland A's
2. A – True
3. C – Cincinnati Reds
4. B – Los Angeles Dodgers (19)
5. A – True
6. D – Los Angeles Dodgers
7. A – True
8. B – 7
9. A – 0
10. D – 8
11. B – 1
12. B – False (They have always been members of the NL West.)
13. A – Troy Tulowitzki
14. C – DJ LeMahieu
15. D – Vinny Castilla
16. A – True
17. B – Jamey Carroll
18. D – 7
19. D – 5
20. A – True

DID YOU KNOW?

1. The Los Angeles Dodgers have the most National League West Division championships with 19. The San Francisco Giants have won 8, the San Diego Padres and Arizona Diamondbacks have 5 and the Colorado Rockies have not won any. The Cincinnati Reds won 7 division championships during their time in the NL West. The Atlanta Braves won 5 division championships during their time in the NL West. The Houston Astros won 2 division championships during their time in the NL West. The most recent NL West Division champions are the Los Angeles Dodgers, who won the 2020 World Series. The Colorado Rockies have earned 5 wild card berths and won 1 NL pennant so far.

2. The Atlanta Braves were the first National League West Division champions in 1969.

3. The Los Angeles Dodgers, San Diego Padres, and San Francisco Giants are all founding members of the National League West Division. The Rockies joined as an expansion team in 1993 and the Arizona Diamondbacks joined as an expansion team in 1998.

4. The Los Angeles Dodgers have earned 2 wild card berths, the San Francisco Giants have earned 3, and the Arizona Diamondbacks and San Diego Padres each have 1 berth.

The Colorado Rockies have the most wild card berths in the NL West with 5.

5. The Colorado Rockies and San Diego Padres are the only teams in the National League West who have NOT yet won a World Series championship.

6. Sandy Alomar, Brett Anderson, John Axford, Jeromy Burnitz, Drew Butera, Jamey Carroll, Craig Counsell, Charlie Culberson, Octavio Dotel, Mark Ellis, Matt Herges, Matt Kemp, Nelson Liriano, Miguel Olivo, Juan Pierre, Scott Podsednik, Juan Uribe, Jamey Wright, and Eric Young Sr. have all played for both the Colorado Rockies and the Los Angeles Dodgers.

7. Sandy Alomar, Yonder Alonso, Clint Barmes, Vinny Castilla, Jhoulys Chacin, Jeff Cirillo, Adam Eaton, Alan Embree, Brad Hawpe, Matt Herges, Nick Hundley, Matt Kemp, Kevin Kouzmanoff, Miguel Olivo, Jay Payton, Drew Pomeranz, Seth Smith, Huston Street, Mark Sweeney, Yorvit Torrealba, John Vander Wal, Greg Vaughn, Todd Walker, Kip Wells, and Eric Young Sr. have all played for both the Colorado Rockies and the San Diego Padres.

8. Jeremy Affeldt, Ellis Burks, Royce Clayton, Tyler Colvin, Charlie Culberson, Andres Galarraga, Darryl Hamilton, LaTroy Hawkins, Charlie Hayes, Matt Herges, Nick Hundley, Mike Kingery, Javier Lopez, Kirt Manwaring, Brent Mayne, Jose Mesa, Gerardo Parra, Neifi Pérez, Kevin Pillar, Drew Pomeranz, Jonathan Sanchez, Marco Scutaro, Scott Servais, Drew Stubbs, Bill Swift, Yorvit Torrealba, Juan

Uribe, John Vander Wal, Jamey Wright, and Eric Young Sr. have all played for both the Colorado Rockies and the San Francisco Giants.

9. Henry Blanco, Eric Byrnes, Jhoulys Chacin, Jeff Cirillo, Royce Clayton, Craig Counsell, Daniel Descalso, Alan Embree, Mike Hampton, Matt Herges, Greg Holland, Chris Iannetta, Joe Kennedy, Brent Mayne, Quinton McCracken, Melvin Mora, Jordan Pacheco, Gerardo Parra, Armando Reynoso, Mark Reynolds, Jorge de la Rosa, and Tony Womack have all played for both the Colorado Rockies and the Arizona Diamondbacks.

10. In 2007, the Colorado Rockies and San Diego Padres played a wild card tiebreaker game after each team finished the season with a record of 89-73. The Rockies beat the Padres by a score of 9-8. This counted as their 90th win on the season. The Rockies went on to appear in the World Series that year against the Boston Red Sox.

CHAPTER 15:

THE AWARDS SECTION

QUIZ TIME!

1. Which Colorado Rockies player won the National League MVP Award in 1997?

    a. Walt Weiss

    b. Dante Bichette

    c. Larry Walker

    d. Andres Galarraga

2. Daniel Bard was named the 2020 National League Comeback Player of the Year.

    a. True

    b. False

3. Who is the only Colorado Rockies player to win the National League Rookie of the Year Award?

    a. Ubaldo Jiménez

    b. Troy Tulowitzki

    c. Todd Helton

    d. Jason Jennings

4. Who is the only Colorado Rockies player ever to win the Hank Aaron Award?

    a. Carlos Gonzalez
    b. Aaron Cook
    c. Todd Helton
    d. Larry Walker

5. How many NL Gold Glove Awards did Nolan Arenado win during his time with the Colorado Rockies?

    a. 5
    b. 6
    c. 7
    d. 8

6. Which Colorado Rockies player won a Silver Slugger Award in 2006?

    a. Todd Helton
    b. Matt Holliday
    c. Jamey Carroll
    d. Clint Barmes

7. No Colorado Rockies player has ever won the Home Run Derby.

    a. True
    b. False

8. Which Colorado Rockies player was named the DHL Hometown Hero (voted by MLB fans as the most outstanding player)?

a. Walt Weiss

b. Dante Bichette

c. Larry Walker

d. Todd Helton

9. Who was the first Colorado Rockies player to win a Gold Glove Award?

a. Larry Walker

b. Neifi Pérez

c. Todd Helton

d. Carlos Gonzalez

10. Who was the first Colorado Rockies player to win a Silver Slugger Award?

a. Dante Bichette

b. Vinny Castilla

c. Ellis Burks

d. Both A and B

11. The Colorado Rockies were named the Baseball America Organization of the Year in which year?

a. 2004

b. 2007

c. 2010

d. 2013

12. No Colorado Rockies player has won the All-Star Game MVP Award.

a. True

b. False

13. Which two Colorado managers won the National League Manager of the Year Award?

    a. Don Baylor and Walt Weiss
    b. Don Baylor and Clint Hurdle
    c. Don Baylor and Jim Tracy
    d. Don Baylor and Bud Black

14. Which Colorado Rockies player was named the 2017 National League Comeback Player of the Year?

    a. Carlos Gonzalez
    b. Jonathan Lucroy
    c. Ian Desmond
    d. Greg Holland

15. Which Colorado Rockies player was the 2013 National League batting champion?

    a. Todd Helton
    b. Michael Cuddyer
    c. Nolan Arenado
    d. Troy Tulowitzki

16. No Colorado Rockies player has ever won a Roberto Clemente Award.

    a. True
    b. False

17. Which Colorado Rockies player was named the 2007 NLCS MVP?

    a. Troy Tulowitzki
    b. Todd Helton

    c. Matt Holliday

    d. Aaron Cook

18. How many Gold Glove Awards did DJ LeMahieu win during his time with the Colorado Rockies?

    a. 1

    b. 2

    c. 3

    d. 4

19. Which Colorado Rockies player won a 1996 Silver Slugger Award?

    a. Andres Galarraga

    b. Eric Young

    c. Ellis Burks

    d. All of the above

20. No Colorado Rockies player has ever won an Edgar Martinez Award.

    a. True

    b. False

QUIZ ANSWERS

1. C – Larry Walker

2. A – True

3. D – Jason Jennings (2002)

4. C – Todd Helton (2000)

5. D – 8

6. B – Matt Holliday

7. A – True

8. C – Larry Walker

9. A – Larry Walker (1997)

10. D – Both A and B (1995)

11. B – 2007

12. A – True (2011)

13. C – Don Baylor and Jim Tracy

14. D – Greg Holland

15. B – Michael Cuddyer

16. A – True

17. C – Matt Holliday

18. C – 3

19. D – All of the above

20. A – True

DID YOU KNOW?

1. No Colorado Rockies pitcher has ever won a Cy Young Award.

2. The Colorado Rockies have had 16 different players win Silver Slugger Awards. They were Dante Bichette, Vinny Castilla, Andres Galarraga, Eric Young, Ellis Burks, Larry Walker, Mike Hampton, Todd Helton, Matt Holliday, Carlos Gonzalez, Troy Tulowitzki, Michael Cuddyer, Nolan Arenado, Charlie Blackmon, Trevor Story, and German Marquez.

3. The Colorado Rockies have had only one player named the National League Rookie of the Year: Jason Jennings in 2002.

4. The Colorado Rockies have had seven different players win Gold Glove Awards: Larry Walker, Neifi Pérez, Todd Helton, Carlos Gonzalez, Troy Tulowitzki, Nolan Arenado, and DJ LeMahieu.

5. The Colorado Rockies have had only one player win an MVP Award: Larry Walker in 1997.

6. The Colorado Rockies have had nine different players win the National League batting titles: Andres Galarraga, Larry Walker, Todd Helton, Matt Holliday, Carlos Gonzalez, Michael Cuddyer, Justin Morneau, DJ LeMahieu, and Charlie Blackmon.

7. The Colorado Rockies have had two players win the National League Comeback Player of the Year Award: Greg Holland (2017) and Daniel Bard (2020).

8. The Colorado Rockies have had two managers win the National League Manager of the Year Award: Don Baylor (1995) and Jim Tracy (2009).

9. Colorado Rockies players/managers/front office staff enshrined in the Colorado Sports Hall of Fame are Jerry McMorris, Bob Gebhard, Keli McGregor, Vinny Castilla, Dante Bichette, Andres Galarraga, Todd Helton, Don Baylor, and Larry Walker.

10. As the 2007 National League champions, the Colorado Rockies as a team won the Warren Giles Trophy.

CHAPTER 16:

THE MILE HIGH CITY

QUIZ TIME!

1. On average, Denver has how many days of sunshine per year?

    a. 200
    b. 250
    c. 300
    d. 350

2. Denver is exactly one mile above sea level.

    a. True
    b. False

3. Which restaurant chain started in Denver?

    a. Chick-Fil-A
    b. Arby's
    c. Subway
    d. Chipotle

4. Every U.S. President since Teddy Roosevelt has visited the Brown Palace Hotel and Spa except for which president?

a. Barack Obama

b. Calvin Coolidge

c. John F. Kennedy

d. Jimmy Carter

5. What is the longest continuous street in the United States?

a. Colorado Blvd.

b. Federal Blvd.

c. Colfax Ave.

d. Santa Fe Drive

6. In Denver's high altitude, golf balls can travel up to how much further than they do at sea level?

a. 5%

b. 10%

c. 15%

d. 20%

7. Denver brews more beer than any other city in the United States.

a. True

b. False

8. What is the name of Denver's NFL team?

a. Denver Broncos

b. Denver Packers

c. Denver 49ers

d. Denver Ravens

9. What is the name of Denver's NBA team?

a. Denver Grizzlies

b. Denver Kings

c. Denver Warriors

d. Denver Nuggets

10. How many Super Bowl championships have the Denver Broncos won?

a. 1

b. 3

c. 4

d. 6

11. What is the name of Denver's NHL team?

a. Colorado Sharks

b. Colorado Rangers

c. Colorado Avalanche

d. Colorado Wild

12. The Denver Nuggets have never won an NBA championship.

a. True

b. False

13. What is the name of Denver's MLS team?

a. Colorado Earthquakes

b. Colorado Rapids

c. Colorado Galaxy

d. Colorado Sounders FC

14. Both the Denver Nuggets and the Colorado Avalanche play at Ball Arena in Denver.

    a. True
    b. False

15. What is the name of the Denver Broncos' stadium?

    a. Allegiant Stadium at Mile High
    b. Arrowhead Stadium at Mile High
    c. Levi's Stadium at Mile High
    d. Empower Field at Mile High

16. Denver has a professional lacrosse team called the Colorado Mammoth.

    a. True
    b. False

17. Denver International Airport is the _____ largest airport in the world.

    a. 2nd
    b. 4th
    c. 8th
    d. 12th

18. What is Denver International Airport's IATA code?

    a. DEA
    b. DIA
    c. DEN
    d. DEI

19. Denver is home to how many parks?

a. 100

b. 150

c. 200

d. 250

20. Over 3,000 animals are housed at the Denver Zoo.

a. True

b. False

QUIZ ANSWERS

1. C – 300

2. A - True

3. D – Chipotle

4. B – Calvin Coolidge

5. C – Colfax Avenue

6. B – 10

7. A – True

8. A – Denver Broncos

9. D – Denver Nuggets

10. B – 3

11. C – Colorado Avalanche

12. A – True

13. B – Colorado Rapids

14. A – True

15. D – Empower Field at Mile High

16. A – True

17. A – 2nd

18. C – DEN

19. C – 200

20. A – True

DID YOU KNOW?

1. Denver has more marijuana dispensaries than Starbucks locations.

2. The Denver Mint makes the most coins in the world.

3. Denver is the "Baby Boomer Capital of America." It has more baby boomers than any other city in the United States.

4. Denver was chosen in 1970 to host the 1976 Winter Olympics but became the first city ever to withdraw its candidacy after winning the bid when it pulled out of hosting duties in 1972.

5. The Colorado State Capitol's dome is plated in real gold. The world's entire supply of Colorado Rose Onyx was used inside the building.

6. There are many conspiracy theories about Denver's airport. When you enter the airport by car, you will see a statue of a blue mustang with red glowing eyes nicknamed "Blucifer" by locals.

7. Colorado's Red Rocks Amphitheater was named the best outdoor concert venue in the United States by *Rolling Stone*.

8. Denver was named the healthiest city for pets in the United States by Purina Petcare.

9. Due to the altitude, it is easier to get drunk in Denver. Drinks can be up to three times more potent in the Mile High City.

10. Denver is home to the annual Great American Beer Festival.

CHAPTER 17:

TULO

QUIZ TIME!

1. What is Troy Tulowitzki's full name?

    a. Troy Tyler Tulowitzki

    b. Troy Trever Tulowitzki

    c. Troy Timothy Tulowitzki

    d. Troy Tucker Tulowitzki

2. Troy Tulowitzki played his entire 13-season MLB career with the Colorado Rockies.

    a. True

    b. False

3. Where was Troy Tulowitzki born?

    a. Long Beach, California

    b. San Diego, California

    c. Oakland, California

    d. Santa Clara, California

4. When was Troy Tulowitzki born?

a. January 10, 1984

b. January 10, 1989

c. October 10, 1984

d. October 10, 1989

5. Derek Jeter was Troy Tulowitzki's favorite baseball player while growing up.

   a. True

   b. False

6. How many Gold Glove Awards did Troy Tulowitzki win during his 13-season MLB career?

   a. 1

   b. 2

   c. 3

   d. 4

7. Which MLB team was Troy Tulowitzki a fan of while growing up?

   a. Los Angeles Dodgers

   b. San Diego Padres

   c. Oakland A's

   d. San Francisco Giants

8. After retiring as a player, Troy Tulowitzki was hired by the University of Texas as an assistant baseball coach.

   a. True

   b. False

9. How many World Series championships did Troy Tulowitzki win during his 13-season MLB career?

    a. 0

    b. 1

    c. 2

    d. 3

10. What year did Troy Tulowitzki make his MLB debut?

    a. 2004

    b. 2005

    c. 2006

    d. 2007

11. How many All-Star Games was Troy Tulowitzki named to during his 13-season MLB career?

    a. 1

    b. 2

    c. 3

    d. 4

12. Troy Tulowitzki attended college at Long Beach State.

    a. True

    b. False

13. How many times was Troy Tulowitzki named the National League Player of the Month?

    a. 1

    b. 2

    c. 3

    d. 4

14. Troy Tulowitzki was named the 2006 Colorado Rockies Minor League Player of the Year.

    a. True
    b. False

15. How many Silver Slugger Awards did Troy Tulowitzki win?

    a. 1
    b. 2
    c. 3
    d. 4

16. How many times was Troy Tulowitzki named the National League Player of the Week?

    a. 2
    b. 3
    c. 4
    d. 5

17. Troy Tulowitzki was named the August 2007 National League Rookie of the Month.

    a. True
    b. False

18. How many home runs did Troy Tulowitzki hit?

    a. 215
    b. 225
    c. 245
    d. 255

19. How many RBIs did Troy Tulowitzki collect?

    a. 720

    b. 750

    c. 780

    d. 800

20. Troy Tulowitzki's career batting average is .290.

    a. True

    b. False

QUIZ ANSWERS

1. B – Troy Trever Tulowitzki
2. B – False (He played for the Colorado Rockies, Toronto Blue Jays, and New York Yankees.)
3. D – Santa Clara, California
4. C – October 10, 1984
5. A – True
6. B – 2
7. C – Oakland A's
8. A – True
9. A – 0
10. C – 2006
11. D – 5
12. A – True
13. B – 2 (September 2010 and April 2014)
14. A – True
15. B – 2
16. D – 5
17. A – True
18. B – 225
19. C – 780
20. A – True

DID YOU KNOW?

1. Troy Tulowitzki stole 57 bases during his 13-season MLB career.

2. Troy Tulowitzki had a total of 4,804 at-bats in his MLB career.

3. Troy Tulowitzki collected 1,391 hits.

4. Troy Tulowitzki's career WAR is 44.5.

5. As a member of Team USA, Troy Tulowitzki won a gold medal in the World University Baseball Classic in 2004.

6. Troy Tulowitzki spent 10 seasons with the Colorado Rockies, three seasons with the Toronto Blue Jays, and one season with the New York Yankees.

7. Troy Tulowitzki's favorite musician growing up was Jay-Z.

8. Troy Tulowitzki made his MLB debut at 21 years old against the New York Mets. He played in his final MLB game at 34 years old against the Detroit Tigers.

9. Troy Tulowitzki played in the All-Star Futures Game in 2006.

10. Troy Tulowitzki was a first-team All-Big West selection in 2004 and 2005.

CHAPTER 18:

CARGO

QUIZ TIME!

1. Where was Carlos Gonzalez born?

    a. Caracas, Venezuela

    b. Maracaibo, Venezuela

    c. Oaxaca, Mexico

    d. Acapulco, Mexico

2. Carlos Gonzalez spent his entire 12-season MLB career with the Colorado Rockies.

    a. True

    b. False

3. What year did Carlos Gonzalez win the National League batting title?

    a. 2009

    b. 2010

    c. 2012

    d. 2014

4. How many Silver Slugger Awards did Carlos Gonzalez win during his 12-season MLB career?

    a. 0
    b. 1
    c. 2
    d. 3

5. How many Gold Glove Awards did Carlos Gonzalez win?

    a. 1
    b. 2
    c. 3
    d. 5

6. How many All-Star Games was Carlos Gonzalez named to?

    a. 1
    b. 3
    c. 4
    d. 6

7. Carlos Gonzalez hit for the cycle on July 31, 2010.

    a. True
    b. False

8. How many World Series championships did Carlos Gonzalez win during his MLB career?

    a. 0
    b. 1

c. 2

d. 3

9. How many home runs did Carlos Gonzalez hit?

    a. 204

    b. 214

    c. 224

    d. 234

10. How many RBIs did Carlos Gonzalez collect?

    a. 755

    b. 765

    c. 775

    d. 785

11. How many total hits did Carlos Gonzalez collect?

    a. 1,332

    b. 1,432

    c. 1,532

    d. 1,632

12. Carlos Gonzalez was 22 years old when he made his MLB debut.

    a. True

    b. False

13. What year did Carlos Gonzalez make his MLB debut?

    a. 2006

    b. 2007

    c. 2008

    d. 2009

14. When was Carlos Gonzalez born?

    a. June 17, 1981

    b. June 17, 1985

    c. October 17, 1981

    d. October 17, 1985

15. How many bases did Carlos Gonzalez steal?

    a. 111

    b. 122

    c. 133

    d. 144

16. Carlos Gonzalez had 5,033 at-bats during his MLB career.

    a. True

    b. False

17. What is Carlos Gonzalez's full name?

    a. Miguel Carlos Gonzalez

    b. Carlos Miguel Gonzalez

    c. Eduardo Carlos Gonzalez

    d. Carlos Eduardo Gonzalez

18. What is Carlos Gonzalez's career batting average?

    a. .265

    b. .275

    c. .285

    d. .295

19. How many times during his MLB career was Carlos Gonzalez named the National League Player of the Week?

a. 1

b. 3

c. 5

d. 9

20. Carlos Gonzalez's career WAR is 24.4.

a. True

b. False

QUIZ ANSWERS

1. B – Maracaibo, Venezuela
2. B – False (He played for the Colorado Rockies, Oakland A's, Chicago Cubs, and Cleveland Indians.)
3. B – 2010
4. C – 2
5. C – 3
6. B – 3
7. A – True
8. A – 0
9. D – 234
10. D – 785
11. B – 1, 432
12. A – True
13. C – 2008
14. D – October 17, 1985
15. B – 122
16. A – True
17. D – Carlos Eduardo Gonzalez
18. C – .285
19. C – 5
20. A – True

DID YOU KNOW?

1. Carlos Gonzalez was named the National League Player of the Month only once in his MLB career: July 2015.

2. Carlos Gonzalez made his MLB debut with the Oakland A's on May 30, 2008, at 22 years old against the Texas Rangers. Carlos Gonzalez played his final MLB game with the Chicago Cubs on June 27, 2019, at 33 years old against the Atlanta Braves.

3. Carlos Gonzalez and his wife, Indonesia, have a boy and twin girls.

4. Carlos Gonzalez signed a minor-league contract with the Seattle Mariners in February 2020. He was released by the Mariners in June 2020.

5. Carlos Gonzalez came in third for the 2010 National League MVP Award. He was behind only winner Joey Votto and Albert Pujols.

6. Carlos Gonzalez was the Rockies' starting left fielder from 2010 to 2014. In 2015, he moved to right field due to the emergence of Corey Dickerson.

7. Carlos Gonzalez had the highest batting average in the National League in 2010 at .336.

8. Carlos Gonzalez's career stolen base percentage is 78.7%.

9. Carlos Gonzalez appeared in 1,247 games for the Colorado Rockies.

10. Carlos Gonzalez appeared in the MLB postseason three years with the Colorado Rockies. He played in the 2009 NLDS, the 2017 NL wild card game, the 2018 NL wild card game, and the 2018 NLDS.

CHAPTER 19:

AMERICA'S PASTIME

QUIZ TIME!

1. How many teams play in Major League Baseball?

    a. 15
    b. 20
    c. 30
    d. 33

2. Major League Baseball was founded in 1903.

    a. True
    b. False

3. Who is the current commissioner of Major League Baseball?

    a. Bart Giamatti
    b. Fay Vincent
    c. Bud Selig
    d. Rob Manfred

4. In what year was the National League founded?

a. 1870

b. 1876

c. 1903

d. 1911

5. In what year was the American League founded?

   a. 1888

   b. 1901

   c. 1903

   d. 1918

6. Major League Baseball is the second wealthiest professional sports league. Which league is the wealthiest?

   a. NBA

   b. NHL

   c. NFL

   d. MLS

7. The Major League Baseball headquarters is located in New York City.

   a. True

   b. False

8. How many games does each Major League Baseball team play per season?

   a. 92

   b. 122

   c. 162

   d. 192

9. In which two U.S. states is Major League Baseball's spring training held?

    a. California and Florida

    b. Arizona and Florida

    c. Arizona and California

    d. California and Arizona

10. How many stitches does an MLB baseball have?

    a. 98

    b. 100

    c. 108

    d. 110

11. Where is the National Baseball Hall of Fame located?

    a. Denver, Colorado

    b. Phoenix, Arizona

    c. Los Angeles, California

    d. Cooperstown, New York

12. All 30 MLB teams are located in the United States.

    a. True

    b. False

13. Which current MLB stadium is the oldest baseball stadium still in use?

    a. Angel Stadium

    b. Dodger Stadium

    c. Fenway Park

    d. Wrigley Field

14. Major League Baseball has the highest attendance of any sports league in the world.

   a. True
   b. False

15. Fill in the blank: Seventh Inning _____

   a. Jog
   b. Song
   c. Shake
   d. Stretch

16. William Howard Taft was the first United States president to throw out the ceremonial first pitch at a Major League Baseball game.

   a. True
   b. False

17. It is a Major League Baseball rule that all umpires must wear _____ underwear in case they rip their pants.

   a. Tan
   b. Gray
   c. White
   d. Black

18. In what year did the first World Series take place?

   a. 1903
   b. 1905
   c. 1915
   d. 1920

19. Former Major League Baseball Commissioner Bart Giamatti is the father of actor Paul Giamatti.

    a. True
    b. False

20. The song traditionally played in the middle of the 7th inning at MLB games is called *Take Me Out to the Ballpark.*

    a. True
    b. False

QUIZ ANSWERS

1. C – 30

2. A - True

3. D – Rob Manfred

4. B – 1876

5. B – 1901

6. C – NFL

7. A – True

8. C – 162

9. B – Arizona and Florida

10. C – 108

11. D – Cooperstown, New York

12. B – False (The Toronto Blue Jays are located in Canada.)

13. C – Fenway Park

14. A – True

15. D – Stretch

16. A – True

17. D – Black

18. A - 1903

19. A – True

20. B – False (*Take Me Out to the Ballgame*)

DID YOU KNOW?

1. The average lifespan of a baseball in a Major League Baseball game is seven pitches. This means approximately five to six dozen baseballs are used in every game.

2. The Boston Americans won the very first Major League Baseball World Series. They defeated the Pittsburgh Pirates in eight games. Today the most games a World Series can go is seven.

3. The New York Yankees currently hold the most World Series titles in Major League Baseball with 27.

4. Hot dogs are the most popular food item sold at Major League Baseball ballparks. Over 21 million hot dogs were sold at MLB stadiums in 2014.

5. The longest MLB game on record occurred on May 9, 1984, between the Chicago White Sox and Milwaukee Brewers. The game lasted 8 hours, 6 minutes. The most innings played in a Major League Baseball game was the 26 innings on May 1, 1920, between the Brooklyn Dodgers and Boston Braves.

6. The pitcher's rubber to home plate distance at MLB ballparks is 60 feet, 6 inches.

7. Before they can be used in a game, each MLB baseball is rubbed with special mud to improve grip and reduce

luster. This special mud comes from a specific, secret location in the state of New Jersey.

8. The fastest MLB game on record took place on September 28, 1919. The game between the New York Giants and Philadelphia Phillies took 51 minutes. An average MLB game is 3 hours.

9. The American League uses a designated hitter. A DH only hits and does not play in the field. In the National League, the pitcher hits instead of there being a designated hitter. If an interleague game is being played, whether a DH is used or not is determined by which team is the home team. If the home team is from the American League, each team will use a DH. If the home team is from the National League, each team's pitcher will hit.

10. The distance between bases in Major League Baseball is 90 feet.

CHAPTER 20:

GOATS

QUIZ TIME!

1. How many World Series championships did Babe Ruth win during his 22-season career?

   a. 3
   b. 5
   c. 7
   d. 9

2. Jackie Robinson's uniform No. 42 was retired by all MLB teams in 1997.

   a. True
   b. False

3. How many All-Star Games was Willie Mays named to during his 22-season MLB career?

   a. 8
   b. 14
   c. 20
   d. 24

4. How many National League batting titles did Tony Gwynn win during his 20-season MLB career?

    a. 2
    b. 6
    c. 8
    d. 10

5. Rickey Henderson holds the all-time MLB record for most stolen bases. How many did Rickey steal during his 25-season MLB career?

    a. 1,306
    b. 1,406
    c. 1,506
    d. 1,606

6. What year was Hank Aaron inducted into the National Baseball Hall of Fame?

    a. 1980
    b. 1981
    c. 1982
    d. 1983

7. Derek Jeter was named the 1996 American League Rookie of the Year.

    a. True
    b. False

8. How many Gold Glove Awards did Ken Griffey Jr. win during his 22-season MLB career?

a. 7

b. 8

c. 9

d. 10

9. How many No-Hitters did Nolan Ryan throw during his 27-season MLB career?

    a. 1

    b. 3

    c. 7

    d. 9

10. Ted Williams missed which season(s) due to military service?

    a. 1943

    b. 1944

    c. 1945

    d. All of the above

11. How many times was Joe DiMaggio named MVP during his 13-season career?

    a. 0

    b. 1

    c. 2

    d. 3

12. Stan Musial spent his entire 22-season MLB career with the St. Louis Cardinals.

    a. True

    b. False

13. In what year was Reggie Jackson inducted into the National Baseball Hall of Fame?

    a. 1990
    b. 1993
    c. 1995
    d. 1999

14. Cal Ripken Jr. spent his entire 21-season MLB career with the Baltimore Orioles.

    a. True
    b. False

15. How many All-Star Games was Roberto Clemente named to during his 18-season MLB career?

    a. 5
    b. 10
    c. 15
    d. 18

16. Johnny Bench spent his entire 17-season MLB career with the Cincinnati Reds.

    a. True
    b. False

17. How many times did Sandy Koufax lead the league in ERA during his 12-season MLB career?

    a. 2
    b. 3
    c. 4
    d. 5

18. Frank Robinson was named the National League Rookie of the Year in which year?

    a. 1955
    b. 1956
    c. 1965
    d. 1966

19. Lou Gehrig spent his entire 17-season career with the New York Yankees.

    a. True
    b. False

20. Rod Carew was named the 1967 American League Rookie of the Year.

    a. True
    b. False

QUIZ ANSWERS

1. C – 7

2. A - True

3. D – 24

4. C – 8

5. B – 1,406

6. C – 1982

7. A – True

8. D – 10

9. C – 7

10. D – All of the above

11. D – 3

12. A -True

13. B – 1993

14. A – True

15. C – 15

16. A – True

17. D – 5

18. B – 1956

19. A – True

20. A – True

DID YOU KNOW?

1. Babe Ruth spent his 22-season career with the New York Yankees, Boston Red Sox, and Boston Braves. He is a member of the National Baseball Hall of Fame, the 1923 American League MVP, two-time All-Star, seven-time World Series champion, the 1924 AL batting champion, and led the league in ERA in 1916. Ruth is often regarded as the greatest baseball player of all time.

2. Jackie Robinson spent his entire 10-season career with the Brooklyn Dodgers. He is a member of the National Baseball Hall of Fame, the 1949 National League MVP, six-time All-Star, 1955 World Series champion, the 1949 National League batting champion, and the 1947 National League Rookie of the Year. Robinson is best known for breaking the color barrier in baseball.

3. Willie Mays spent his 22-season career with the San Francisco Giants and New York Mets. He is a member of the National Baseball Hall of Fame, two-time MVP, 1951 National League Rookie of the Year, 24-time All-Star, 1954 World Series champion, 12-time Gold Glove Award winner, the 1954 National League batting champion, two-time All-Star Game MVP, and the 1954 Major League Player of the Year.

4. Tony Gwynn spent his entire 20-season career with the San Diego Padres. He is a member of the National Baseball Hall

of Fame, 15-time All-Star, five-time Gold Glove Award winner, seven-time Silver Slugger Award winner, and eight-time batting champion.

5. Rickey Henderson spent his 25-season career with the Oakland A's, New York Yankees, San Diego Padres, New York Mets, Boston Red Sox, Los Angeles Dodgers, Anaheim Angels, Seattle Mariners, and Toronto Blue Jays. He is a member of the National Baseball Hall of Fame, the 1990 American League MVP, two-time All-Star, and two-time World Series champion. Henderson is often regarded as the greatest leadoff hitter of all time. He holds the MLB record for most stolen bases.

6. Hank Aaron spent his 23-season career with the Atlanta Braves and Milwaukee Brewers. He is a member of the National Baseball Hall of Fame, the 1957 National League MVP, 25-time All-Star, 1957 World Series champion, two-time NL batting champion, and three-time Gold Glove Award winner.

7. Derek Jeter spent his entire 20-season career with the New York Yankees. He is a member of the National Baseball Hall of Fame, 14-time All-Star, 1996 American League Rookie of the Year, five-time World Series champion, the 2000 World Series MVP, the 2000 All-Star Game MVP, five-time Gold Glove Award winner, and five-time Silver Slugger Award winner.

8. Stan Musial spent his entire 22-season career with the St. Louis Cardinals. He is a member of the National Baseball

Hall of Fame, three-time MVP, 24-time All-Star, three-time World Series champion, seven-time batting champion, and two-time Major League Player of the Year.

9. Cal Ripken Jr. spent his entire 21-season career with the Baltimore Orioles. He is a member of the National Baseball Hall of Fame, two-time MVP, 19-time All-Star, 1982 American League Rookie of the Year, 1983 World Series champion, two-time Gold Glove Award winner, eight-time Silver Slugger Award winner, two-time All-Star Game MVP, and two-time Major League Player of the Year.

10. Sandy Koufax spent his entire 12-season career with the Los Angeles Dodgers. He is a member of the National Baseball Hall of Fame, the 1963 National League MVP, three-time Cy Young Award winner, three-time Triple Crown winner, seven-time All-Star, three-time World Series champion, two-time World Series MVP, five-time National League ERA leader, and two-time Major League Player of the Year.

CONCLUSION

Learn anything new? Now you truly are the ultimate Rockies fan! Not only did you learn about the Rockies of the modern era but you also expanded your knowledge back to the early days of the franchise.

You learned about the Colorado Rockies' origins and their history, including where they came from. You learned about the history of their uniforms and jersey numbers and read some crazy nicknames. You learned more about the legendary Todd Helton. You also learned about Hall of Famer Larry Walker. Plus, who could forget Troy Tulowitzki and Carlos Gonzalez? You were amazed by Rockies stats and recalled some of the most famous Rockies trades and draft picks of all time. You broke down your knowledge by outfielders, infielders, pitchers, and catchers. You looked back on the Rockies' playoff feats and the awards that came before, after, and during them. You also learned about the Rockies' fiercest rivalries, both within their division and outside it.

Every team in MLB has a storied history but the Colorado Rockies have one of the most memorable of all. They have gone through winning seasons and losing seasons with the backing of their devoted fans. Being the ultimate Rockies fan takes knowledge and a whole lot of patience, which you tested with this book. Whether you knew every answer or were stumped by several questions, you learned some of the most interesting history that the game of baseball has to offer.

The deep history of the Colorado Rockies franchise represents what we all love about the game of baseball. The heart, the determination, the tough times, and the unexpected moments, plus the players who inspire us and encourage us to do our best because, even if you get knocked down, there is always another game and another day.

With players like Trevor Story, Charlie Blackmon, and Jon Gray, the future of the Colorado Rockies continues to look bright. They have a lot to prove but there is no doubt that this franchise will continue to be one of the most competitive teams in Major League Baseball year after year.

It's a new decade, which means there is a clean slate, ready to continue writing the history of the Colorado Rockies. The ultimate Rockies fan cannot wait to see what's to come for their beloved team.

Made in United States
Orlando, FL
22 December 2023

41607971R00093